Stages in the Evolution of Plant Species

Stages in the

EVOLUTION OF
PLANT SPECIES

BY *Jens Clausen*

CARNEGIE INSTITUTION OF WASHINGTON

DEPARTMENT OF PLANT BIOLOGY

STANFORD, CALIFORNIA

CORNELL UNIVERSITY PRESS

Ithaca, New York, 1951

Preface

THESE essays were presented as lectures under the Messenger Foundation at Cornell University during November, 1950. The principles outlined are the outcome of experiments on plants carried out during a period of nearly twenty years at the Division of Plant Biology of the Carnegie Institution of Washington and, earlier, for about ten years at the Department of Genetics of the Royal Agricultural College, Copenhagen, Denmark.

The experiments at the Carnegie Institution were planned and executed in co-operation with my two colleagues, Dr. David D. Keck and Dr. William M. Hiesey. It was my unusual good fortune to find colleagues of such vision, such different approaches, and such independent thinking who were willing to enter into mutual co-operation on problems that transcend the range of individual fields. I owe a deep debt of gratitude for their contribution toward the development of principles and basic philosophies that underlie the experiments and the interpretation of results. Through daily discussion and gradual accretion, such principles were built into a coherent structure, and the ideas here presented are therefore the product of integrated group thinking. Dr. Hiesey, moreover, has critically read the manuscript and contributed many valuable suggestions, and Dr. Keck has participated in the formulation of conclusions presented in the charts.

The facts and the conclusions presented in these essays are primarily based on experiments and studies on many groups of plants from very different environments by the author and his colleagues. Some of the discussion represents re-evaluations of previously published experiments, but much is based on unpublished data from our experiments, which later will be presented in a more thoroughly documented and detailed form.

The recent monumental publication by Dr. G. Ledyard Stebbins, Jr., *Variation and Evolution in Plants,* makes it unnecessary to review the very extensive literature on this subject. The reader is therefore referred to this excellent monograph and to the already classic work, *Genetics and the Origin of Species,* by Dr. Th. Dobzhansky. The conclusions of Professor Irene Manton from her broad investigations in a special field, as presented in her recent book, *Problems of Cytology and Evolution in the Pteridophyta,* are so similar to the facts extracted from our experiments on the much more recently evolved Spermatophyta that it is evident that even in the most diverse groups of plants the fabric of life has much in common.

The drawings and photographs in the present book are largely the products of the skill of Mr. James D. Harris of the Art Department of Stanford University and Mr. Berton Crandall of Palo Alto, respectively.

JENS CLAUSEN

Stanford, California
January 25, 1951

Contents

Stages in the Evolution of Plant Species

Introduction

THE origin of things alive has challenged the imagination of man for a long time. Many are the theories that have been proposed to account for the amazing variability of living things. The geological record gives us the major story of how one group of organisms followed another, but very little is known about the details of how distinct species arise. Until recently even very little has been known about the nature of species and what sets them apart. Only rarely do we witness the rise of a new species, and those whose origin we have observed are of a special kind. Also, only in a very few cases have we been able to find a complete record of how a species is connected with its past, and our life is too short to enable us to see how it may change into a species of the future.

The taxonomists recognize some 300,000 species of higher plants. Compared with the estimated five million species of insects, the kinds of plants seem to be small in number. But each of these species fits into its own range of habitats, and together they cover the earth from the tropical to the arctic regions. They include types of plants as different as the grasses, roses, and sunflowers, and as pines, oaks, and palms.

In many instances these very different forms of plants must have reproduced their own kind during millions of years, for we can recognize some of them in fossil records of ancient date. On the other hand, we know they all have the potential ability to change.

For these reasons we are faced with a paradoxical living world that is mutable in its immutability. Perhaps that is why Charles Darwin in 1859 referred to the origin of species as "that mystery of mysteries." The experimental investigations conducted since Darwin have not materially changed the aptness of this characterization of the species problem. In fact, the investigations since Darwin have revealed a variability in living things infinitely richer than his generation could realize. Even the species itself is no longer the basic biological unit, for most species have been found to be composed of complexes of races, each of which in itself is in delicate balance with its environment.

The record of evolution is preserved not only in the paleontological impressions of dead species in the strata of the earth but, more important still, also in the species and races which are now alive. This latter part of the record rests on the observed relationships between species as they exist today and represents a relatively instantaneous picture of a single stage in their evolution. Although we are limited in our ability to interpret the species of the present in terms of their past and their future, we can nevertheless utilize the study of the current stages in evolutionary differentiation successfully to reconstruct some of the gaps in the fragmentary record of the past.

Taking the theory of evolution as valid, we should expect to find living species in all stages of distinctness. We should be able to discover some of the beginnings of differentiation leading to the species of the future and to discover other species and groups of species that are in the process of passing out. We should expect to find groups of species with many still closely related components, and others in which only a few more remotely related species remain. Live species, and especially live plant species, have the great advantage over fossil forms that one can use them for experimental analysis and try to take them apart and put them together again in order to discover what makes them function as species.

These considerations have been the basic philosophy behind the Carnegie Institution experiments. Through the experiments, we have found that there are natural entities of plants in all stages of differentiation, and that there are a great many different kinds of patterns of evolutionary differentiation. An outstanding feature of living things is that there are so many ways in which they are able to fit themselves to their environment and to set themselves apart from each other. The particular type of organization that keeps them in balance with their environment, and that also keeps them apart as biological groups, is determined by a great many factors, often in the form of elaborate systems of checks and balances that keep each other in dynamic equilibrium.

Such systems provide a considerable degree of resiliency within the species, a flexibility that can take care of minor maladjustments and even major exigencies and that also contributes to the ability of individuals to tolerate moderate changes in the environment. When the environments change, this flexibility or range of tolerance makes it possible for living things to persist until the hereditary constitution of their offspring can shift to fit the new environmental conditions on a more permanent basis.

Our conclusions are based on a great number of experiments in growing plants of many kinds from very contrasting environments, and in both uniform and contrasting gardens. They are also based on many crossings between plants in all stages of evolutionary differentiation, using plants of many families. The data from more than 300 hybrids of our own experiments are supported by data from the experiments of many other scientists which have been reported in the literature of the last 30 years. In many cases the conclusions with regard to evolution were not drawn, because the papers were written with other objectives in view. Despite this apparent wealth of information, our knowledge concerning the dynamics of evolution is still limited and fragmentary. In the following pages, we shall attempt to present the picture of evolution as our group of investigators sees it and to extrapolate with theory at a few points where theory may be helpful to the understanding of the whole picture.

The Evolution of

Our Concepts of Speciation

BEFORE we enter into a consideration of the various stages in the evolution of plant species, it is desirable to present a thumbnail sketch of the development of evolutionary concepts as it has occurred from the time of Linnaeus until some thirty years ago, when a series of new concepts regarding evolution was ushered in.

Linnaeus— It is generally assumed that Linnaeus always was an advocate of the concept of the immutable species. This is based upon his youthful arbitrary definition of species in *Classes Plantarum* in 1738 ("There are as many species as there were originally created diverse forms"). His followers remembered this statement and cited it, whereas they forgot his later work. In his mature years he started to hybridize distinct species of plants, and the insight he gained thereby caused him radically to change his concept. In *Systema Vegetabilium* of 1774 he states the problem of the origin of the species as follows:

Let us suppose that the Divine Being in the beginning progressed from the simpler to the complex; from few to many; similarly that He in the beginning of the plant kingdom created as many plants as there were natural orders. These plant orders He himself, therefrom producing, mixed among themselves until from them originated those plants which today exist as genera.

Nature then mixed up these plant genera among themselves through

4

generations of double origin [= hybrids] and multiplied them into the existing species, as many as possible (whereby the flower structures were not changed) excluding from the number of species the almost sterile hybrids, which Darwin produced by the same mode of origin.

This forgotten evolutionary theory antedates Darwin's by nearly 100 years, but most of the students who followed Linnaeus were too busy naming and classifying plants to appreciate the statements of his later years concerning the importance of experiments.

The early hybridizers— Thousands of crossing experiments conducted by Linnaeus (1760, 1790), and especially by J. G. Koelreuter (1761–1766) and C. F. Gaertner (1849), showed that plants which botanists usually classify as distinct species were either unable to intercross or produced more or less sterile hybrids. On the other hand, varieties belonging to one species were easily crossed and yielded perfectly fertile offspring. The discovery of the interspecific barriers to interbreeding was a major step in our understanding of the organization of living things, but the significance of these barriers was not fully recognized. Even today there are some geneticists and taxonomists who are unwilling to recognize the significance of such barriers.

Alexis Jordan, discoverer of the local population— Jordan (1846) tested the degree of constancy of plants grown from seeds harvested from series of local populations of several species of violets and pansies in France. He found such populations to be distinct and relatively constant, and because in that day these were considered to be the criteria of species, he named the populations accordingly. During the years 1860–1873 he published a great number of species of *Draba* (later *Erophila*) on the basis of similar experiments. Jordan had actually discovered the fact that species are composed of a great number of recognizably different local populations, but his interpretation that these populations were distinct species confused the species concept and discredited him in the eyes of most taxonomists.

Charles Darwin, exponent of the significance of natural selection— Interest in Jordan's experimental investigations on species composition was sidetracked by the appearance of Darwin's *The Origin of Species,* published 1859. This book started a new era in biology by the stimulating new viewpoints it presented. Darwin himself was experimentally inclined, but his followers were not, and for nearly half a century biologists concentrated on a descriptive study of comparative morphology as they tried to solve all the problems of the descent of species. In his discussions of what constitutes a species, Darwin himself seems not to have appreciated fully the significance of the sterility barriers between species, for at that time he was more interested in emphasizing the transitions between species than in studying the relative barriers between them.

Darwin's specific contribution to our understanding of evolution was his emphasis on the great wealth of natural variation and the significance of natural selection in determining which part of this variation will survive.

Gregor Mendel, discoverer of the units of inheritance— The kind of impetus given to biology by the writings of Darwin and the early evolutionists was so strong that Mendel's discovery in 1865 of the two basic principles that determine heredity and produce some of the needed variability for natural selection was overlooked, and accordingly did not influence the thinking of biologists for 35 years to come. It was not until De Vries, Correns, and Tschermak (1900) independently rediscovered the Mendelian laws that new light was focused on the theory of evolution. The early hybridizers of distinct species had dealt with complex heredities produced by a mosaic of small differences, giving the over-all effect of blending inheritance. Through a fortunate choice of material, however, the differences analyzed by Mendel were determined by a very few units of heredity, and each of these had such marked effects that he could demonstrate that the hereditary units were distinct from each other and that they could be combined into a hybrid, separated again in the progeny, and interchanged in various combinations in succeeding generations. The professional taxonomists were slow in recognizing the significance of these basic discoveries for the understanding of the organization of species. One exception was a brilliant amateur botanist, Dr.

Ezra Brainerd, president of Middlebury College in Vermont, who in 1904 showed that in certain closely related species of *Viola* the taxonomic key differences between the species were determined by Mendelian units of inheritance and that in natural hybrids these differences recombined in new ways to produce new species.

Pure lines, and the concepts of genotype, phenotype, and genes— In 1901–1902 Wilhelm Johannsen started experiments designed to test experimentally the claims that selection itself would produce variation. For these experiments Johannsen chose an old cultivated strain of beans, the Princess strain, because it presumably had pollinated itself for many generations and therefore should be constant and homogeneous. Johannsen found that even such a strain was composed of a great many heritably different but constant substrains, which he called pure lines. His initial selection within this commercial strain gave rise to pure lines differing in their mean seed weight over a range of 35 to 65 centigrams. However, when he selected small and large beans from the same self-fertilizing individual, the small and the large seeds produced plants having essentially the same seed weight, not significantly different from the mean seed weight of the mother plant. Johannsen (1903, 1905, 1911) concluded that there are two kinds of variation, namely, one that is inherited, with which selection is effective until pure lines have been obtained, and another, a nonhereditary one which he called fluctuating variability, with which selection is not effective. The outcome of these experiments was a clarification of the difference between inherited variation, determined by Mendelian genes, and nonheritable variation, the modifications determined by the environment. Natural selection is without effect in the absence of genetic variation. Johannsen concluded that the phenotype of an individual, or its external appearance, is the product both of its heredity, that is, its genotype, and of its environment. Natural selection acts on the phenotype, but it is the genotype that determines the character of the offspring.

Hybrid cytology and the rise of cytogenetics— There are several ways in which the study of the chromosomes has contributed to our understanding of the evolutionary processes. In 1902, W. A. Cannon, W. S. Sutton, and M. F. Guyer had independently suggested that the regular pairing and distribution of the chromosomes to the two daughter nuclei when sex cells are being formed provides a mechanism that can account for Mendelian inheritance. The work of T. H. Morgan (1911, 1915), his associates, and many others has provided acceptable proof for this theory and has expanded the concept through the study of linkage groups and crossing-over phenomena.

Another correlation between chromosomes and evolution was discovered by Otto Rosenberg (1903, 1904, 1909) in the pairing of chromosomes in natural interspecific hybrids between two species of *Drosera,* or sundew, a plant of bogs. *Drosera rotundifolia* has 10 pairs and *longifolia* twice as many, or 20 pairs, of chromosomes. On a trip in 1900 to Tromsö in Norwegian Lapland, Rosenberg studied the sterile hybrid between these two species which was growing between both parents and found that it had 30 chromosomes, having received 10 from one and 20 from the other parent species. When pollen or egg cells were being formed, the chromosomes of the hybrid lined up as 10 pairs and 10 singles. The single chromosomes were distributed at random to the sex cells, which thus received anywhere from 10 to 20 chromosomes, but none of the cells, not even those with 10 or 20 chromosomes, as in the parents, were viable.

Along a third way, in 1917 Öjvind Winge called attention to the fact that related plant species of one genus often differ from each other by chromosome numbers in multiples of a basic number that may vary from one genus to another. He suggested that new species in such an arithmetic series could arise through hybridization between species whose chromosomes were unable to interpair in the hybrid; if all the chromosomes in such a hybrid doubled, then each unpaired chromosome would be provided with a partner, and normal pairing, constancy, and fertility should be restored. Such a hybrid, later called an amphiploid (= "both folded together"), would be a double organism, having combined the unlike inheritances of both parents in a self-perpetuating organism. By thus adding unrelated sets of chromosomes together the polyploid series of chromosome numbers could have arisen. Here was another theory useful for testing the connection between genetics and the function of chromosomes. The validity of this theory has since been amply demonstrated in many families of plants.

The study of mutations— Natural selection is only the negative half of the theory of evolution, and Johannsen's experiments made it clear that selection in itself does not produce anything new. Obviously, selection cannot continue to go on unless new genes are forthcoming to select from and to combine with old genes. A long line of investigations on gene changes have been carried out, ranging from H. de Vries's observations of mutants in the evening primroses (1901–1903) beginning in 1887, to H. J. Muller's induction of mutations in 1927–1928 through radiation and variation in temperature, and to Erwin Baur's and Tine Tammes's observations in 1924–1925 of frequent spontaneous mutations of minute but additive effects in snapdragon and flax. Very different phenomena have been included under the catch-all term of mutation, ranging from the addition, change, or loss of a single gene to the addition, repatterning, or loss of a whole chromosome or a set of chromosomes. The latter group of changes only recombines the basic genes that already are in existence, but the former produces something new.

The discovery of the ecological race— From the beginning of the study of taxonomy and evolution, biologists interested in these lines of investigation had always been thinking primarily in terms of morphological differences, and it was not until Göte Turesson's inception in 1921–1922 of investigations on ecotypes of many genera and families that it was realized that it is the physiological fitness of a plant to its environment that is important for its survival, rather than morphological traits. Turesson (1922, 1925, 1931) and others showed that widespread species are composed of series of contrasting ecological races, the existence of which enable the species to occupy ecologically contrasting environments. The ecological race is now commonly recognized as a basic element in evolution.

The new fields of genetics and cytology had, during the first 20 years of this century, made new tools available for testing the conclusions of the early experimentalists, but for a number of years neither orthodox taxonomists nor orthodox geneticists seemed to be aware of these possibilities. A synthesis of the viewpoints of taxonomy, ecology, cytology, genetics, and physiology was required in order to initiate new investigations, which had to start at the point where Jordan and Gaertner had left them nearly a century ago.

III

The Local Population as the Basic Evolutionary Unit

MOST species are not uniformly distributed over the territory they occupy. They exist as geographically more or less isolated populations in places where they find congenial conditions. This is very evident in regions with a rugged topography, where neighboring populations of a species are often miles apart. Some local populations consist of millions of individuals, others of relatively few, and in the case of annuals the number of individuals in a local population may vary greatly from one year to the next.

Each local population of a species has probably been started by a limited number of individuals, and it may be effectively isolated from other colonies by spatial isolation, although occasionally its supply of hereditary variation may be augmented by introductions of new biotypes from its neighboring populations. The distinctness of a local population and its amount of variability will depend on several factors. Foremost is the kind and number of individuals that first appeared. Other factors to be considered are the maximum and minimum numbers of individuals of that species in the community over a period of years, the particular kind of mutations and other hereditary changes that take place in the individuals of the population, the kind of selection that is dominant in the community, and, finally, the breeding structure of the population, whether self- or cross-pollinating, and the kind of pollinating agent. Any one of these factors may result in populations that are as morphologically distinct from each other as the kind that Alexis Jordan named as species. These differences are not always clearly evident in the wild, but they become very obvious when a number of strains of one species are grown adjacent to each other in one garden. Theoretical calculations on the supposed genetic effects of local isolation have been undertaken by Sewall Wright (1932, 1940) and others, but there are few investigations on record from which one can judge whether or not the facts fit the theories.

The pattern of variability in a series of local populations will probably vary according to the pollinating agent and the breeding structure of the population. Self-pollinating and partially apomictic plants will tend to have a fair number of individuals of certain biotypes represented in a population, but in highly cross-pollinating species hardly two individuals of a population will have the same genetic constitution, and only a limited number of the biotypes that are potentially possible as genetic recombinations would be found at any one time. Among wind-pollinated conifers, which have pollen so light that it is carried for many miles, one should also expect to find less differentiation into highly localized populations than in insect-pollinated plants, but no reliable information on this point is yet available.

Layia— A striking example of great variation in the number of individuals that compose local populations of an annual species is found in *Layia Munzii* Keck, a recently discovered species of the sunflower family that grows in semidesert regions of California. The existence of this spring-flowering annual was originally known from a single specimen, but its natural habitat was sought in vain during 1934 and 1935 in a valley between the inner Coast Ranges of California which was known to be its type locality. During these years the annual rainfall at this locality was only about 5 centimeters. In an alkaline mud flat there, another remarkable and hitherto unknown tarweed species, *Hemizonia Halliana* Keck, was instead discovered, and a photograph of its habitat was taken in 1935 (fig. 1, top). This rare species, which covered some five square miles, was present in fair abundance in both 1934 and 1935.

Fig. 1. Annual variation in the frequency of *Layia Munzii* near Cholame, San Luis Obispo County, California, in an alkaline flat, the type locality of *Hemizonia Halliana* and *Layia Munzii. Top,* Dr. David D. Keck collecting seeds of *Hemizonia Halliana* in 1935 when no Layias were present. *Bottom,* same locality in 1936 densely covered with *Layia Munzii* between the *Hemizonia.*

In 1936, a year in which the rains were more plentiful, the long-sought *Layia Munzii* appeared in abundance among the *Hemizonia Halliana* plants (fig. 1, bottom) in this same valley. In this particular habitat, which turned out to be the alkaline flat from which the type specimen had originally come, two square miles were densely covered with *Layia Munzii,* and it formed also good stands in other localities in the same general arid region of California that year, where it had been missing the preceding years. Obviously tremendous fluctuations in the size of the populations of this species take place from year to year. Similar fluctuations in population size occur in a related species, *Layia leucopappa* Keck, which is a rare native of the dry southern foothills of the Sierra Nevada. In seasons when these two species are abundant there are hundreds of thousands of individuals per population, but in unfavorable years they seem to be completely absent.

Morphological differences between local populations of a species are illustrated by examples of basal leaves of *Layia gaillardioides* DC. in figure 2. The leaves of the three populations on the left are from the outer Coast Range, and those on the right are from the inner Coast Range. Each leaf is from a different individual, and each population is represented by only a small sample of its 60 individuals actually grown. All populations were grown beside each other in the Stanford garden and were started at the same time. It will be seen that each population is variable but that it nevertheless is clearly distinguishable from the others. Such population differences extend to other characters, as well. For example, the rays of the flower heads vary in color without any apparent relation to geographic significance. In the population from Saratoga Summit and Isabel Creek, the rays were golden yellow throughout, whereas the plants from Muir Beach had lighter-colored greenish-yellow rays. The three other populations had rays with golden-yellow bases and lighter-colored tips, namely, greenish yellow in Tomales, almost white in Knoxville, and pure white in the Lewis Creek population. The plants from the outer Coast Range are late-flowering and have thick, succulent stems, whereas those from the inner Coast Range are early-flowering and have much thinner stems. These latter differences are correlated with ecological differences between the outer and the inner Coast Range.

The size of the individual populations of *Layia gaillardioides,* on the one hand, and of *Munzii* and *leucopappa* on the other, are

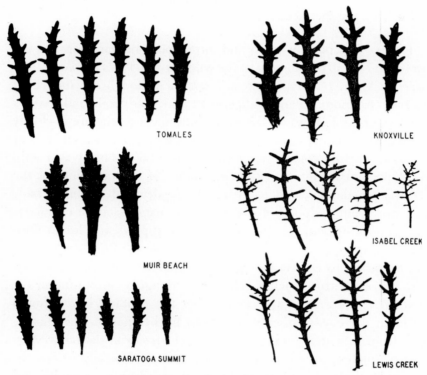

Fig. 2. Inter- and intrapopulation variation of six populations of *Layia gaillardioides* as shown by basal leaves. Each leaf is from a different individual. *Left,* leaves of three populations from the outer Coast Range of central California. *Right,* leaves of three populations from the inner Coast Range. The populations are arranged from north to south with the northernmost at top. All leaves are from plants grown in the Carnegie Institution garden at Stanford.

approximately the same during favorable years, but the latter two species have much greater annual fluctuations in the size of their populations because they occupy a semidesert area where annual differences in rainfall become limiting. All three species consist of cross-breeding, self-incompatible individuals, and their populations are geographically equally well isolated. According to current theories, the smaller populations of *Munzii* and *leucopappa* in poor years should favor relatively greater genetic differences between their populations, but actually they show very little variation. The differences between the larger populations of *gaillardioides,* on the other hand, are very spectacular.

Viola— Conspicuous inter- and intrapopulation variation was observed in Danish populations of the wild pansies, *Viola tricolor* L. and *arvensis* Murr. (Clausen, 1921 and 1922). Although *tricolor* has 13 pairs of chromosomes and is a species of acid, sandy soils, and *arvensis* has 17 pairs and grows on calcareous soils, these species are so closely related that spontaneous intercrossing takes place wherever they meet, and hybrid colonies are found on neutral or faintly acid soils. The spontaneous intercrossing contributes to the variability of the natural populations, and its effect can be detected at considerable distances from the point of contact. More than a score of characters vary, including some as spectacular as the stipules and leaves illustrated in figure 3.

The variations tend to be regionally relatively localized. The stipules of *tricolor,* for instance, tend to be triangular in outline in the southwestern corner of the country, but this characteristic is found again in the Faeroe Islands, 800 miles farther north. The stipules vary from palmately divided (fig. 3 *b*) in *tricolor* in the far western part of Jutland, to pinnately lobed (3 *a*) as *tricolor* approaches the region of *arvensis,* to pinnately dissected with largely expanded end lobe (3 *e*) in many forms of *arvensis,* and to peculiarly pinnate structures with large, leaflike end segments (3 *d*) in a moor population of *arvensis.* On one small island, an *arvensis* form with palmate stipules similar to those of *tricolor* was found on acid soil. The many variable characters of the wild pansies open possibilities for literally millions of morphologically different recombinations, although only a fraction of these are actually found in wild populations at any one time.

Some of the variation in the wild pansies is correlated with differences in environment, but other differences appear to be fortuitous.

Fig. 3. Variation in shape of stipules and leaves in the *Viola tricolor* complex: *a,* pinnately divided stipules in a form of *V. arvensis; b,* palmately divided stipules in the western Jutland form of *V. tricolor; c,* small stipules and leaves of the maritime dune race of *V. tricolor; d,* leaflike end lobes on a moor form of *V. arvensis; e,* very large, pinnately divided stipules with enlarged end lobe in an island form of *V. arvensis* from sand. All from Denmark. (From Clausen, 1922.)

In *Viola tricolor,* the inland form (fig. 4 *a*) is early-flowering, has large leaves and an erect habit, and is an annual, whereas the plants from wind-swept coastal dunes are late-flowering, have small leaves, pointed or acuminate lower petals, and a low habit, and are perennial. In one coastal area they achieve the low habit (fig. 4 *b, c*) by producing stems having a strong downward turgor, which causes them to hug the ground; in another locality the plants have transversally geotropic stems with very long nodes that spread over the dunes, and in still another wind-swept dune area the stems are erect but have exceedingly short nodes and therefore have a low habit. All of these forms are distinct populations of a maritime dune race. These populations are 200 and 30 miles apart, respectively, the erect form with short nodes being on a small island 20 miles from the mainland. Also, on this island several populations had developed notched lateral petals, a character determined by several genes and found only on plants in an area five miles across, with the highest percentage in the center of the area. The frequencies at three points of sampling were 42, 72, and 4 per cent.

Potentilla glandulosa— This species of the rose family is composed of series of local populations scattered widely through western North America. A great number of populations from California were sampled and 60 individuals of each were grown in the garden at Stanford. Figure 5 shows one basal leaf per individual from a series of Stanford-grown populations originating from various altitudes. Four morphological subspecies are involved, each represented by several local populations. Within each subspecies there is considerable intrapopulation variation as to shape of leaf, number of pinnae per leaf, size and density of leaflets, and similar characters.

One can match certain leaves from one population with certain ones from another, and to some extent also from one subspecies to another, but sufficient differences still remain to make the subspecies stand out as recognizably different entities. To a smaller extent, the populations within a subspecies are also distinct. The leaves are only one of many characters that vary from plant to plant within one population. Other variations include pubescence and color of stem,

Fig. 4. Variation associated with habitat differences in *Viola tricolor* from Denmark: *a*, the erect inland form, an annual; *b*, the perennial dune form having depressed habit; *c*, a single stem of the dune form, which grows horizontally as soon as it emerges from the sand. These inland and dune races were found in juxtaposition with only a road between them. (From Clausen, 1922.)

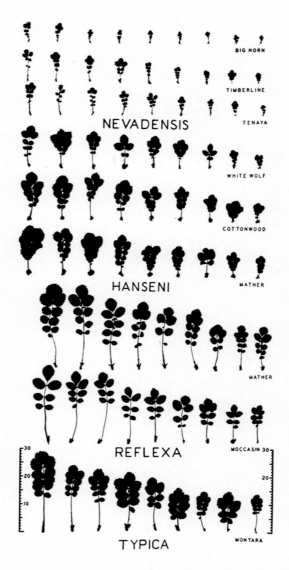

Fig. 5. Inter- and intrapopulation variation in basal leaves of four subspecies of *Potentilla glandulosa* from a west-to-east transect across central California. Each leaf is from a different individual grown in the Carnegie Institution garden at Stanford. Localities: Montara, at 900 feet altitude in the outer Coast Range; Moccasin, at 900 feet in the foothills of the Sierra Nevada; Mather, at 4600 feet in the yellow pine belt of the Sierra Nevada, *reflexa* on sunny slopes, *Hanseni* in meadows; Cottonwood, at 6000 feet; White Wolf, at 8000 feet; Tenaya, at 8200 feet; Timberline, at 10,000 feet; Big Horn, at 11,000 feet altitude (the latter near permanent snow patches).

size and shape of petals, color shades of petals, and size and color of seeds. Many other species show similar hereditary variations within and between populations. Such differences are accentuated and therefore most easily studied on spaced plants growing in a uniform garden. In populations growing in the wild it is impossible to distinguish between modifications induced by the environment and differences due to heredity.

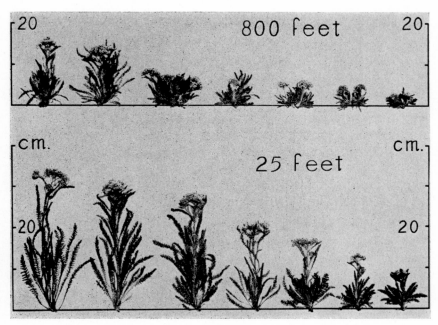

Fig. 6. Inter- and intrapopulation variation in *Achillea borealis* from Kiska Island in the Aleutians in the North Pacific at 52° N. latitude. The plants were grown in the Carnegie Institution garden at Stanford from seeds collected on Kiska by Dr. Malcolm Nobs. (From Clausen, Keck, and Hiesey, 1948.)

Achillea borealis— The milfoils or yarrows are cross-pollinating plants of the sunflower family with light, winged seeds that can be carried easily by wind. The Achilleas have extensive, almost continuous populations in many localities. Figure 6 shows individual variation within two populations of *Achillea borealis* on Kiska Island in the Aleutians. The vegetation on this treeless, wind-swept island consists entirely of low-growing plants. Samples consisting of 7

Stanford-grown plants of two distinct populations originally collected at two altitudes are shown; the plants represent the range of variation among the 60 individuals grown from each population (Clausen, Keck, and Hiesey, 1948).

The individuals of the two populations vary in dimensions and shapes of leaves, pubescence, width of inflorescence, size and color of rays, earliness of flowering, degree of dormancy during the winter, and length of stems. It will be seen that in the population from 800 feet altitude there are individuals with sessile inflorescences, a very unusual characteristic in *Achillea*. The race from the lower altitude is the taller, has the larger and less pubescent leaves, remains the more winter-active at Stanford, and clearly represents a form ecologically distinct from the population from the higher altitude. It is evident, nevertheless, that some of the smallest plants from the low altitude can be matched with the taller ones from higher up. The two populations are nevertheless statistically clearly distinct, even though their variabilities overlap.

It is probable that the intrapopulation variation enables a species to tolerate periodic variations in the climate at any one locality. In fact, differences in range of tolerance were actually observed among individuals of *Achillea borealis* originally from a maritime bluff in California when transplanted to the Mather station situated at 4500 feet altitude in the Sierra Nevada, for in this very different climate some individuals were much less retarded in growth than others. There is need for more exact investigation along these lines.

Layia platyglossa— There are very few experimental investigations on the genetic variability within and between populations of a species throughout its territory. In most cases either the sampling has been too scattered and incomplete or else the samples were taken in the wild and not grown in a uniform garden. In the latter case no clear distinction can be made between the differences caused by heredity and those that are due only to differences in the environments under which the plants were grown. Conclusions based on plants taken in the wild are therefore of only limited value in determining heritable variability.

One of the better-sampled species is *Layia platyglossa* (F. et M.) Gray, the spring-flowering California tidytips of the *Compositae*. This species is an annual that in its native habitat germinates during the winter rain period, flowers in spring, and dries up in late May. It is obligatorily cross-pollinating, and, like almost all Layias, it occurs in isolated populations or colonies which range in size from a few hundred to millions of individuals, depending upon the year and the location. As a rule, each population is geographically well separated from its nearest neighbor by a distance of from four to ten miles or more, so that there is very little interpopulation pollination and each colony becomes a biological unit in itself. One of the commonest *Layia* species, *platyglossa* is scattered over an area about 100 miles wide and 600 miles long in California, in addition to an extension into Baja California some 200 miles long.

Layia platyglossa occurs therefore over several geographic and climatic zones in a topographically varied region, as the relief map of California (fig. 7) so vividly shows. Its range includes the windswept bluffs of the coast of the Pacific Ocean, the slopes of the outer and inner Coast Ranges south of San Francisco, and the broad San Joaquin Valley between the Coast Ranges and the Sierra Nevada. Moreover, the San Gabriel and San Bernardino Mountains, running from west to east across southern California, effectively separate by massive barriers the colonies of *platyglossa* into northern and southern groups of populations.

Throughout this topographically varied region many natural populations of this species were sampled by collecting seeds from as many individuals as possible within a colony, mixing the seeds thoroughly, and growing a sample of 60 individuals from each colony in the uniform garden at Stanford. Some of the strains were grown for several successive years.

The variations between populations of nine characters studied in this manner on uniformly spaced plants are listed and graphed in figure 8. The populations are arranged in five ecological and geographical groups to show the composite differences between these groups. The graphed data represent means for the populations.

The 4 populations of the maritime race are from wind-swept bluffs and span a north-south distance of 300 miles. They are late-flowering, have no central stem or leader, and accordingly are of low height. Many plants tend to have 13 instead of 8 rays per head, the usual

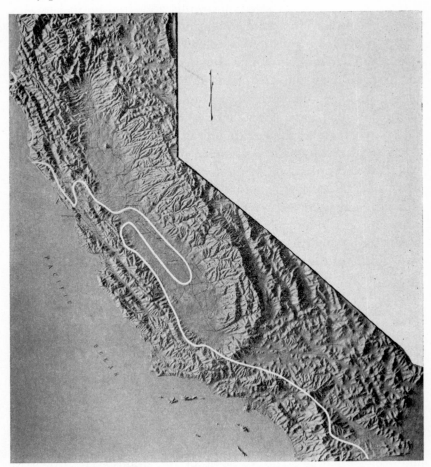

Fig. 7. Relief map of California with the area of *Layia platyglossa* southwest of the white line. (Map reproduced by permission of the Department of Geology, Stanford University.)

number for more inland populations. These coastal races also have a much greater number of disk florets per head, and the heads are supported by thicker, more succulent peduncles than in the other groups of populations. The 3 populations from exposed hilltops in the outer Coast Range but at some distance from the sea are medium-late-flowering, decumbent in habit, and generally without a central leader, but nevertheless they are considerably taller than those from the bluffs. On the whole, they also have fewer 13-rayed plants and fewer disk florets per head than the maritime populations, but these characteristics tend to vary fairly independently from one population to the next.

The 14 inner Coast Range populations flower two to three weeks earlier than those from the coastal bluffs and are taller, having an erect leader; they also have fewer ray and disk florets per head. There is considerable random variation between populations in this group, as shown by the zigzag pattern of the lines in the graphs in figure 8, which indicates that there are no distinct differences in trend between populations from this group.

Only two populations from the subtropical San Joaquin Valley were studied, and they are similar in most respects to the plants from the two Coast Ranges. In common with races of other genera from the same region, however, they are taller and have fewer disk florets per head.

All four groups of populations from north of the San Bernardino Mountains are similar in having pappus of nonpubescent bristles and uniformly black anthers. South of this range we find a morphologically different complex that is extremely variable. Most of the populations south of this line vary in relation to both the pubescence of the pappus bristles and the anther color, for they contain some plants with floccose or cottony pappus and others that are nonfloccose, some that have black and others that have yellow anthers. Most populations contain all four recombinations of these characters but in very different proportions. The nonfloccose individuals from southern California are genetically different from the nonfloccose forms north of this line, although morphologically they are alike. This difference will be discussed in Chapter V.

The populations from south of the San Gabriel–San Bernardino Mountains differ also from those north of these mountains by the longer white tips and a lemon-yellow base south of these mountains as compared with shorter tips and chrome-yellow bases north of the mountains. In color of the base of the rays, however, the San Bernardino and Etiwanda populations of the southern group resemble the populations north of the mountains.

Other characteristics that distinguish the southern group of populations from the northern group are fewer inner bracts subtending the disk florets, fewer pappus bristles per disk floret, and fewer disk florets per head. The peduncles that carry the heads are also more slender.

The curves shown in figure 8 connect the means for each population, and the variations in the lines indicate random difference between populations of the same geographical group. There are a good number of other characters in this species that also vary from plant to plant and from population to population, but those shown on the chart suggest the general pattern of variation.

It is evident that the major breaks that characterize the differences between the five principal groups are of a higher order than the smaller random ones that distinguish populations of the same climatic or geographic zone from each other. Accordingly, ecological zones and geographic barriers correlate with the more conspicuous morphological or statistical differences. Some of the discontinuities are expressed in floral characters such as anther color and pappus, neither of which appear to be associated with differences in ecology, but others are concerned with such characters as growth habit and earliness of flowering, which do show ecological correlations.

Much discussion has appeared in the literature concerning clines, which are conceived of as being gradients of variation of individual characters along an ecological or geographical transect (Huxley, 1940). Much of the evidence for clines has been based on sampling of too few populations taken too far apart. In other cases, the measurements were made on materials growing in the wild and therefore subjected to uncontrolled modifications in many environments. In the wild strains of *Layia platyglossa* grown in a uniform garden, where the influence of differences in the environment in producing modifications was reduced to a minimum, there is no discernible gradient for most of the characters, but rather a zigzagging back and forth combined with fairly abrupt changes at certain points. These

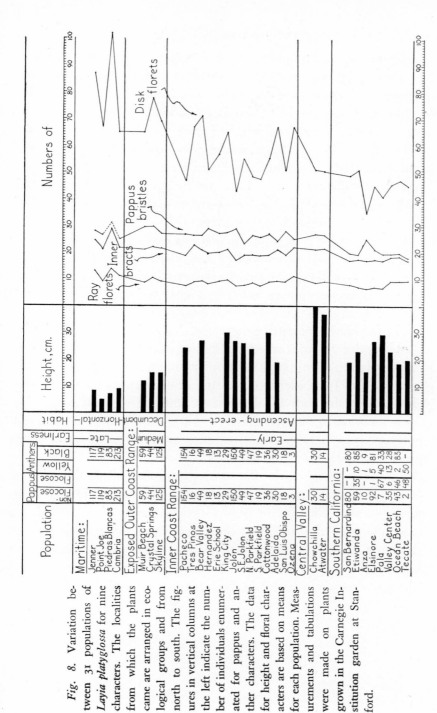

Fig. 8. Variation between 31 populations of *Layia platyglossa* for nine characters. The localities from which the plants came are arranged in ecological groups and from north to south. The figures in vertical columns at the left indicate the number of individuals enumerated for pappus and anther characters. The data for height and floral characters are based on means for each population. Measurements and tabulations were made on plants grown in the Carnegie Institution garden at Stanford.

27

variations between populations of the same group appear to be of minor ecologic significance and to depend largely on chance frequency of distribution of various biotypes from one colony to another.

The term cline can be used only for individual characters, and not for an assemblage of characters of groups of individuals such as a series of populations, for a single individual may with respect to one character belong to one cline and with respect to another character to a different cline. Clines are therefore not commensurable with natural entities, and are oversimplified abstractions dealing with the variation of individual characters.

The five major groups of populations of *Layia platyglossa* show characteristic trends in variability and these indicate the beginning of evolutionary discontinuities. Such discontinuities are superimposed on the intrapopulation variation of a lesser order.

The facts here presented concerning the local populations of a few plant species are confirmed by studies on many other groups of plants. Not only do the populations within one ecological area of a species differ from each other in minor characteristics, but there is also considerable individual variation within each local population. Such variations have been found to characterize both cross- and self-pollinating species, and even populations of apomictic species that propagate as clones.

It is at the level of the local population that all of the selective forces act upon the genetic resources of the population. The survivors may, however, include many biotypes, because each biotype has a certain latitude of tolerance. Because many local populations are well separated spatially, they constitute rather effectively isolated breeding units. The most distinct of these may in time become the forerunners of new entities of higher order.

IV

The Evolution of Ecological Races

SOME species of plants have a very limited distribution and occupy only a limited climatic zone. Other species range far and wide and occupy zones from the lowlands to the alpine, from the seacoast to the interior of the continents, and from warm-temperate to arctic environments. What is it that makes some species so cosmopolitan and others so limited in distribution?

Thirty years ago it was generally believed that one could convert lowland forms to alpines, and vice versa, simply through transplantation, and Gaston Bonnier's experiments (1895) were cited as proof. In 1922, Göte Turesson published his first report on the races of saltbrush and hawkweeds, pointing out that the species were composed of heritably distinct races which he called ecotypes. Turesson concluded that each race was particularly well fitted for survival in its own environment. Independently of Turesson, similar investigations on Danish wild pansies, *Viola tricolor,* had led to the same conclusion (Clausen, 1922).

It is now established as a general biological law that species that occupy many kinds of environment are able to do so because they have evolved series of physiologically distinct races, each of which survives within its native zone but is less able to compete in neighboring zones and usually is unable to survive in the extreme ranges of the species. This fitness is primarily physiological; it is determined by genes, and it may or may not be expressed in the external appearance of the plant. Ecological races or ecotypes have therefore generally been overlooked by taxonomists, geneticists, and ecologists, all of whom looked for visible characters that they could classify. Actually, however, the ecological race is a far more important biological entity than the morphological subspecies.

An ecological race is usually composed of a considerable number of variable local populations existing within a given ecological zone. It represents the next stage in evolutionary differentiation above the local population.

Turesson observed that when "habitat types" or races from contrasting environments were transplanted to a uniform garden, they still remained different. He attributed such differences to "the sorting and controlling effect of the habitat factors [= the factors of the environment] upon the heterogeneous species-population" (1925). He noted that plants of many genera and families had developed parallel races in environments of the same kind, as, for example, dwarf, early-flowering races in alpine and arctic environments, low, prostrate, late-flowering races along exposed coastal bluffs, and tall, erect, medium-early races in inland lowlands.

Similar and even more strongly differentiated races than in northwestern Europe were discovered in California, also on the western side of the continent (Clausen, Keck, and Hiesey, 1940, 1948). Because of the more southern latitude and the higher mountains with their intervening valleys, a much greater variation in climates exists in California than in northern Europe, and a correspondingly greater number of races are present. These ecological races can be satisfactorily recognized only by experiment, for they are seldom as clearly recognized in the wild as in a uniform garden where they can be directly compared.

Climatic races of Achillea— One of the best and most complete examples of a series of ecological races is found among the yarrows or milfoils in the genus *Achillea* of the sunflower family (Clausen, Keck, and Hiesey, 1948). The *millefolium* complex of this genus is circumboreal in distribution, and has been able to occupy more environments than any other group of higher plants thus far studied. Accordingly, it has evolved many diverse races. In North America the

Achilleas range in latitude at least from southern Mexico at 20° N. to Herschel Island north of Alaska at 70° N., and in altitude from sea level to 11,000 feet at the tree line. They grow in the moist, highly equitable maritime climates of the coast, and extend to the dry, highly continental desert basin. The yarrows range in size from alpine dwarfs a few centimeters tall to giants as tall as a man, but the variation is so gradual that taxonomists have not been successful in recognizing distinct species based on morphological characters.

Populations of *Achillea* were sampled across the state, and 60 individuals of each were grown in the experiment garden at Stanford from localities at approximately 1000-foot intervals in altitude. In this manner it was possible to study both the variation within each population and the differences between populations and races. Figure 9 shows the races as they appear in the Stanford garden. The vertical frequency diagrams indicate the variation in height within each population. The individual of each race which is shown represents the mean height of each population. Thirty individuals from each population were also cloned and grown for four years at three transplant stations, namely, Stanford at sea level, Mather at 4600 feet, and Timberline at 10,000 feet altitude; this test made it possible to determine the approximate range of tolerance of each individual. Key individuals were also cloned and tested by Hiesey under different conditions in the controlled greenhouses of the California Institute of Technology at Pasadena, California. These conditions differed in day-and-night temperatures and in periods of illumination. The controlled experiments made it possible to discover the requirements for differences in day-and-night temperatures of the various races.

The races from the coastal side of the outer Coast Range, where fog and cool temperatures prevail, grow actively all year around. They do so even at Stanford, which lies within the natural range of a normally summer-dormant race. The period of most active growth of the coastal races occurs, however, during the cool, rainy winter. Correspondingly, in the temperature-controlled greenhouses, the coastal races developed best under cool days and nights. The forms from the exposed, coastal bluffs are more compact and of a shorter stature than those from protected places just slightly removed from the coast.

In the valleys of the inner Coast Range and the foothills on both sides of the Great Valley is a rapidly developing winter-active, summer-dormant race that becomes dormant as temperatures rise and water becomes scarce in late May or early June.

The tall, gray-pubescent race of the bottom lands of the subtropical San Joaquin Valley has been called *Achillea gigantea* Poll., but it is in reality a form of *A. borealis* Bong. This San Joaquin Valley strain is green the entire year when grown at Stanford, but is most active during the warmest part of the summer. It flowers much later than the foothill form, which meanwhile has already become summer-dormant. In experiments under controlled conditions it was found that the San Joaquin Valley strain grows best with warmer nights than are optimum for the coastal forms.

As one leaves the digger pine and Douglas oak savannahs of the foothills and enters the transition zone of coniferous forests at 3000 feet altitude in the Sierra Nevada, the annual rainfall increases markedly as compared with the semidesert region of the low foothills. The Achilleas above 3000 feet are also different from those in the foothills and have only 18 pairs of chromosomes as compared with the 27 pairs in the races occurring from the coast to the foothills and taxonomically are referable to another species, *Achillea lanulosa* Nutt. The 18-chromosome *lanulosa* from 3000 feet is very similar morphologically to the adjacent 27-chromosome *A. borealis* from the foothills, but this *lanulosa* race differs from the neighboring *borealis* race physiologically by remaining active both summer and winter. The winters at 3000 feet are still mild, and in January the temperatures reach just slightly below the freezing point.

The Mather population of *A. lanulosa* comes from a meadow at the Mather station at 4600 feet where during the winter months the mean minimal temperatures drop below freezing for about three or four months. Accordingly, this population consists of a mixture of individuals, some of which are winter-active and others winter-dormant when grown in the mild climate of the Stanford station.

All populations of *Achillea* from altitudes of 6400 feet or higher are uniformly summer-active and winter-dormant, even when grown at Stanford. In their inherent seasonal periodicity they are therefore

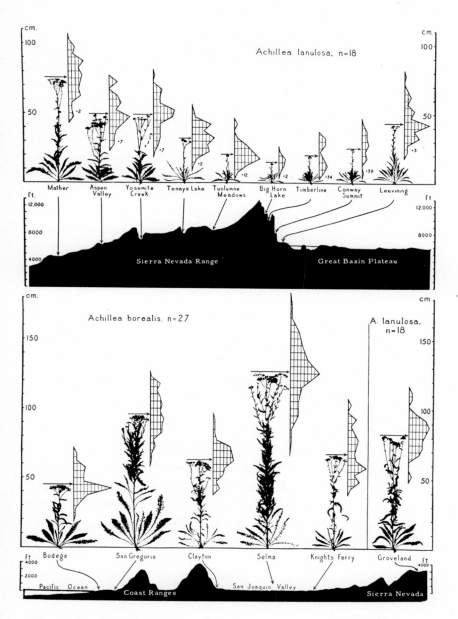

Fig. 9. Altitudinal climatic races of *Achillea* from a west-to-east transect across central California. The arrows indicate the origin of the population on a profile of California. The frequency diagrams indicate variation in height within the populations in the Carnegie Institution at Stanford, and the plant specimens represent the means. The figures to the right of some frequency diagrams indicate the number of nonflowering plants. (After Clausen, Keck, and Hiesey, 1948.)

exactly the opposite of the winter-active, summer-dormant race. Forms from altitudes of 6400 and 7200 feet grow well at mid-altitudes and survive well at the alpine station, but they flower too late at the highest altitude to set ripe seed except during a few exceptionally long summers. Under controlled temperatures the plants from 4600 to 7200 feet develop best when the days are warm and the nights cold. These are also the conditions in their native habitats during spring and early summer when they grow most vigorously and begin to flower. They are all rather susceptible to injury from late-summer or early-fall frosts at the alpine station, but these strains contain a few individuals that are either quite frost-resistant or especially early in flowering, characteristics that are typical of populations native to the highest altitudes.

The forms from altitudes of 8000 to 11,000 feet have narrow, gray leaves and have been recognized taxonomically as a distinct sub-species, *alpicola* (Rydb.) Keck. They are able to set ripe seed in the short summer at high altitudes, are moderately or highly frost-resistant, and emerge in vigorous growth after the winter dormancy there, which is approximately nine months long. They become dormant for only two or three months in the mild climate at Stanford, but emerge in a weakened condition when they resume active spring growth early in March.

The population from 11,000 feet altitude stands out from the other *alpicola* populations as a somewhat distinct race. It flowers earlier at all three stations, and has the shortest stems and the largest percentage of frost-resistant plants. The populations from 8000 to 10,000 feet may be regarded as belonging to a subalpine race, and the one from 11,000 feet to an alpine. Single individuals of the alpine type are found in subalpine populations, so it seems evident that the alpine race is a product of direct selection of biotypes from populations of subalpine altitudes. Under controlled greenhouse experiments it was found that forms from 7000 feet or higher flower only when provided with adequate supplementary light; the forms from lower altitudes flowered freely during shorter days as well.

The populations from the east flank of the Sierra Nevada and the Great Basin plateau live in climates with a short but warm summer.

In controlled conditions, plants of a Great Basin race were found to develop rapidly when the days were hot and the nights relatively warm, conditions that simulate the midsummer of their native environment. Clones of the same plants remain stationary in growth under cool days and nights, in contrast with the plants from the California coast, which are at their best under such conditions. Related Achilleas from the far northern latitudes of Denmark and Lapland resemble the Great Basin plants physiologically in being warm-weather forms that utilize the short but warm growing season available to them for extremely fast growth and development.

Observations on the growth of cloned individuals of the various climatic races of *Achillea* at the Stanford, Mather, and Timberline transplant stations were most revealing in showing differences in the ranges of tolerance of each race and each individual to different climates. Figure 10 illustrates the responses of seven representative individuals of the tall race from the coastal side of the outer Coast Range. The plants shown are dried herbarium specimens of the experimental plants collected as they were grown at each of the three stations. The lower line shows the growth responses at the Stanford station near sea level, the middle line at Mather at 4600 feet, and the top line at Timberline at 10,000 feet altitude. In the lowlands, represented by Stanford, this race is able to utilize both the summer and the winter for growth, but at the mid-altitude station it is forced into winter dormancy for about six months by the cold winter. This race from the cool coastal region is nevertheless able to grow enough during the warm Mather summers, where day temperatures can rise to 38° Centigrade, to store enough food reserves to carry it through the winter. At the alpine station almost all the plants of the coastal races die during the first winter after transplanting. This race is therefore most vigorous at the lowland Stanford station, is reduced in vigor but survives at Mather, and dies in the alpine environment. Individual differences in vigor of growth of this race are especially evident at Mather, which apparently represents an environment close to the limits of tolerance for the survival of the coastal race.

The populations from the inner Coast Range and the foothills have an even more difficult time at Mather because they are forced into

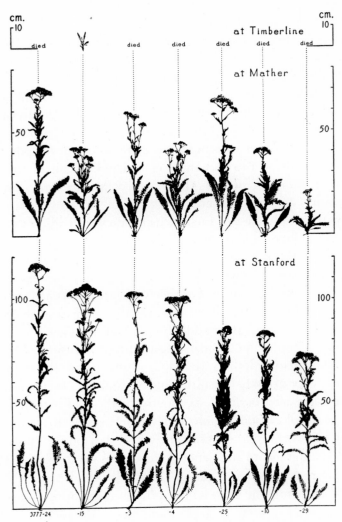

Fig. 10. Responses of 7 cloned individuals of a coastal population of *Achillea borealis* from San Gregorio, San Mateo County, California, when transplanted to the environments of the Carnegie Institution stations at Stanford, Mather, and Timberline. The dotted lines connect members of the same clone grown at the three stations. (After Clausen, Keck, and Hiesey, 1948.)

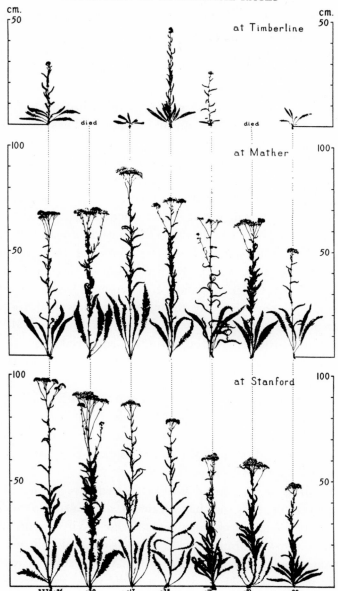

Fig. 11. Responses of 7 cloned individuals of a mid-montane population of *Achillea lanulosa* from Mather, Tuolumne County, California, at 4600 feet altitude when transplanted to the environments at Stanford, Mather, and Timberline. (After Clausen, Keck, and Hiesey, 1948.)

dormancy both by the cold winter and by the hot summer. The short period in spring favorable for the growth of this race is not enough to enable it to survive the two dormancy periods. Physiologically, therefore, the coastal and foothill races are very different, although morphologically they are similar.

All the races from the coast to the foothills become reduced in vigor at mid-altitude and die at the alpine station. They are obviously unable to store enough food during the short growing season to last them for the long winter of approximately nine months at Timberline. A few plants of the race from 3000 feet in the Sierra Nevada, on the other hand, are barely able to survive at the alpine station for two or three years, but they, too, eventually die.

The race from Mather at 4600 feet is most vigorous in growth at its native mid-altitude station, as illustrated by the specimens shown in figure 11. Moreover, it is the most vigorous of the populations of the transect at this particular station. It is also more definitely tolerant of the alpine climate than are the races from lower altitudes, for approximately 50 per cent of its individuals survive there, although they develop too slowly for the setting of ripe seed; also, they are very susceptible to frost injury there, although relatively frost-resistant individuals are found in the population.

The alpine race from 11,000 feet, as shown in figure 12, is distinctly most vigorous at the alpine station. Its individuals are considerably reduced in size when grown at Stanford, and they are barely able to flower in the conditions at Mather, in marked contrast with races from lowland to mid-altitudes.

The Achilleas across central California therefore consist of a remarkable array of races that have seasonal and diurnal periodicities that fit the periodicities of their very diverse environments. Along this 200-mile transect a minimum of 11 physiologically distinct races can be recognized, although taxonomists have difficulty in recognizing even the two species, *Achillea borealis* with 27 pairs and *A. lanulosa* with 18 pairs of chromosomes.

The fitness of the races of *Achillea* for survival in the various environments does not depend upon a single character but on a summation of interrelated physiological characters; in the subalpine environments from 8000 to 10,000 feet altitude it may happen that one individual develops slower than the others, but this handicap may be counterbalanced by greater resistance to frost; another individual in the same population may be frost-susceptible, but nevertheless succeeds because it develops fast enough to mature its seeds before freezing weather starts. In the extreme alpine environment at 11,000 feet, however, short stems, speedy development, and frost resistance are all necessary to ensure survival in a climate with such an extremely short season of growth.

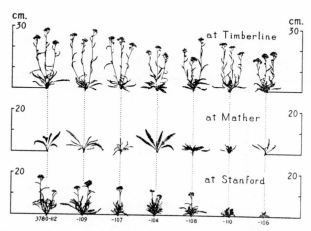

Fig. 12. Responses of 7 cloned individuals of an alpine population of *Achillea lanulosa* from Big Horn Lake, Mono County, California, at 11,000 feet altitude when transplanted to the environments at Stanford, Mather, and Timberline. (After Clausen, Keck, and Hiesey, 1948.)

The local population, at any one place, is composed of many biotypes. This genetic heterogeneity is expressed not only in variable morphological characters but also in differing physiological characteristics, as, for example, frost resistance and earliness of flowering. This kind of variation is revealed most clearly in the capacity of different cloned individuals for growth in the contrasting environments of the transplant stations. An illustration of individual variability among two adjacent climatic races of *lanulosa* is shown in figure 13. Each of the two populations is represented by seven individuals grown at Stanford. The population below is from Yosemite

Creek at 7200 feet in the fir zone, and the one above is from Tenaya Lake at 8200 feet, in the lodgepole-pine zone. These two represent neighboring populations that show overlapping variation, yet they mark a change in race from upper mid-altitude to subalpine.

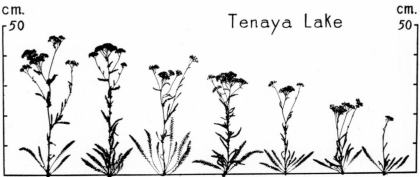

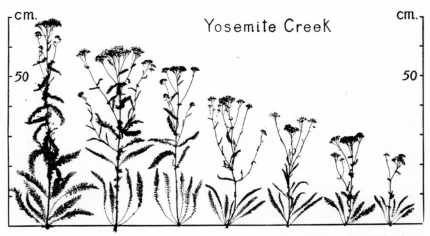

Fig. 13. Individual variability among two adjacent climatic races of *Achillea lanulosa. Above,* the Tenaya Lake population, originally from 8200 feet, and, *below,* the Yosemite Creek population from 7200 feet altitude, both on the western slope of the Sierra Nevada, California. All the plants were grown from seed in the Carnegie Institution garden at Stanford. (After Clausen, Keck, and Hiesey, 1948.)

Figure 14 shows individual graphs of stem heights of 15 cloned individuals of each of these two populations at the three transplant stations, and also a graph of the averaged heights of the two populations as a whole, based on the records of all the 30 individuals of each population that were cloned and grown. The stem heights are indicated by the columns: black for Stanford, crosshatched for Mather, and stippled for Timberline.

The mean heights of the populations as a whole do not reveal the very contrasting patterns of reaction of the component individuals

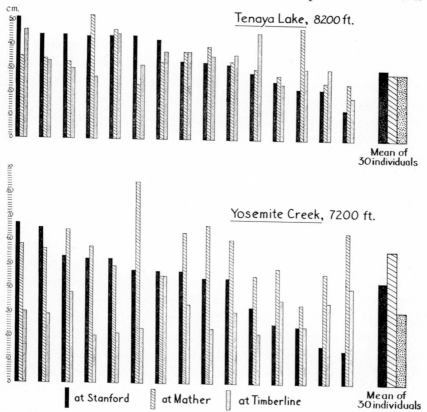

Fig. 14. Graphs of stem heights of 15 cloned individuals of two races in three contrasting climates, and the mean heights of 30 individuals of these races in the same three climates. See text. (Based on data from Clausen, Keck, and Hiesey, 1948.)

at the three stations. Some of the clones grow tallest at the lowland station, others at mid-altitude, and still others at Timberline. In the Tenaya Lake race the averaged heights of all the plants are approximately the same at each station. This apparent statistical uniformity, however, masks the great individual diversity that in itself is of much evolutionary significance for the population, for in certain years one individual will develop most successfully, in other years another. Similarly, over a period of years there is no statistically significant difference in height at Timberline between the Tenaya Lake and the Timberline races, even though they originally grew at altitudes 1800 feet apart. In milder years, the Tenaya Lake population will be definitely taller and more vigorous at Timberline than the one native to the vicinity of this station, but in colder years the Timberline race will be the taller. Individuals within each population will also similarly change their relative ranks as to size and vigor of growth.

Although such extensive individual variability exists within both the Tenaya Lake and the Yosemite Creek populations, the two differ significantly in height at both Stanford and Mather, as shown by the columns representing the means. Moreover, in earliness of flowering the two populations differ significantly at all three transplant stations.

Relatively little change takes place in the Achilleas as one moves up the mountains from 8000 to 10,000 feet altitude, for the next two populations are essentially like the one from Tenaya Lake. Likewise, as one moves downward, the Aspen Valley population at 6400 feet is rather similar to the one from Yosemite Creek in its responses at the transplant stations, whereas the Mather population, coming from 4600 feet, is distinctly different from both. A significant ecological change occurs between the Yosemite Creek and Tenaya Lake populations, for over a relatively short distance we witness a change from the race of the Canadian life zone to one of the Hudsonian zone. Such breaks are nevertheless not abrupt, for individual plants of essentially subalpine type can be found down at Yosemite Creek, and individual plants of the extreme alpine type at Tenaya Lake. A dynamic equilibrium, therefore, apparently exists both within the local population and between ecological races.

Such equilibriums are of significance not only for the survival of the population and of the race in a climate that varies from year to year, but they enable the population and the race to shift in composition, in the course of time, with major environmental changes connected with slow geological changes.

Parallel races in different species— One of the strongest lines of evidence that the environment is the selective agent in evolution is the fact that different species may evolve parallel ecological races in parallel environments. The North American Achilleas belong to two species, *Achillea borealis* and *A. lanulosa,* which differ in chromosome number (W. E. Lawrence, 1947). *A. borealis* is largely a coastal species (fig. 15), and occupies the islands of the North Pacific and a small strip along the west coast of North America as far south as Santa Barbara, California. *A. lanulosa* is continental, but comes to the coast in southern Oregon and seems to have pushed the other species off the continent there. In central California, however, *Achillea borealis* has expanded its beachhead into a large bulge across the Great Valley and, accordingly, has produced four contrasting ecological races.

Achillea borealis and *lanulosa* have evolved parallel ecotypes or climatic races in similar kinds of environment, as shown in figure 16. Where *lanulosa* comes to the coast, it has developed a maritime, late-flowering, short-stemmed race on exposed bluffs, a race that closely mimics the maritime race of *borealis.* It has also evolved a tall and winter-active race in the mild coastal valleys of Oregon, as *borealis* has in California. *A. lanulosa* appears to have nearly a monopoly on alpine races on account of its continental character, but *borealis* has nevertheless succeeded in evolving a true alpine race on the extinct volcanoes of the Aleutian Islands. The parallelism between climatic races in the two species of *Achillea* strongly indicates that a basic evolutionary principle is involved.

Potentilla glandulosa— This is another species containing many ecological races that parallel those in *Achillea.* It is a perennial herb of the rose family and a close relative of the strawberry. Across the central California transect four subspecies occur that are distinct both morphologically and ecologically (Clausen, Keck, and Hiesey, 1940). Representatives of each of these four subspecies and their reactions at the Stanford, Mather, and Timberline transplant stations are shown in figure 17.

Subspecies *typica* Keck occupies the Coast Ranges of California

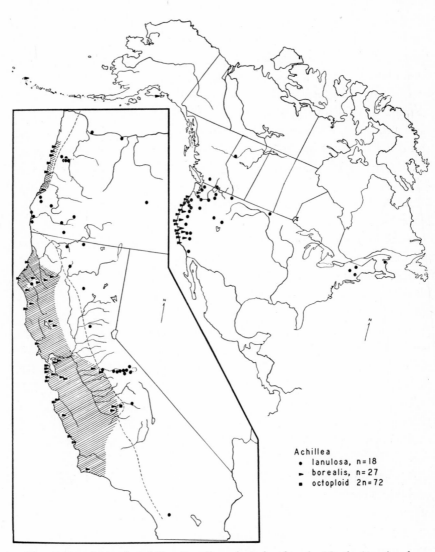

Achillea
• lanulosa, n=18
▬ borealis, n=27
▪ octoploid 2n=72

Fig. 15. Localities of *Achillea borealis* and *A. lanulosa* in North America from which chromosome counts have been made. A single octoploid individual was found in a locality between the areas of *borealis* and *lanulosa*. (From W. E. Lawrence, 1947.)

Fig. 16. Parallel variation in *Achillea lanulosa* (*above*) and *A. borealis* (*below*). *Left,* maritime races; *center,* tall inland races; *right,* alpine races. (From W. E. Lawrence, 1947.)

45

FAILS
TO
SURVIVE

FAILS
TO
SURVIVE

AT STANFORD
El. 100 ft.

AT MATHER
El. 4600 ft.

AT TIMBERLINE
El. 10,000 ft.

Fig. 17. Responses of four ecotypic subspecies of *Potentilla glandulosa* to the three contrasting environments in the Carnegie Institution gardens at Stanford (*left*), Mather (*center*), and Timberline (*right*). The four subspecies are: *nevadensis* from 10,000 feet altitude (*top row*), *Hanseni* from Mather at 4600 feet (*second row from top*), *reflexa* from 2500 feet in the foothills (*third row from top*), and *typica* from 900 feet altitude in the outer Coast Range at Montara (*bottom row*). (Adapted from Clausen, Keck, and Hiesey, 1940.)

and isolated localities in the foothills of the southern Sierra Nevada; *reflexa* (Greene) Keck occurs on warm, sunny slopes of the foothills and mid-altitudes of the Sierra Nevada from 900 to about 6000 feet altitude. *Hanseni* (Greene) Keck is a meadow form occurring between the 4000- and 8000-foot altitudes, and *nevadensis* (S. Wats.) Keck is a high-altitude meadow or slope form from 8000 to 11,000 feet. The organization of altitudinal races in *Potentilla* differs from that in *Achillea* because *Potentilla* has morphologically distinct subspecies. Two of the *Potentilla* subspecies overlap in altitudinal distribution but they occupy different niches, one occurring on slopes and the other in meadows.

Unlike *Achillea*, *Potentilla* does not occupy the exposed coastal strip, the drier east side of the inner Coast Range, or the bottom lands of the Great Valley. The Coast Range subspecies *typica* is a form with large leaves, glandular herbage, congested inflorescences, and small, erect, whitish petals. It is both winter- and summer-active. There are at least three climatic races within this subspecies, namely, one in the outer Coast Range, one in the inner Coast Range, and another in the foothills of the southern Sierra Nevada.

Subspecies *reflexa* of the warm, dry mountain slopes has a taller, more divaricate habit, more open inflorescences, and small, deeply yellow, reflexed petals. It is composed of at least two climatic races; there is a winter-active race in the lower foothills and a winter-dormant race higher up, starting with the *ponderosa* pine at 3000 feet, a point that is about a thousand feet below where winter-dormant races in *Achillea* begin. The meadow subspecies *Hanseni*, which is native at mid-altitudes in the Sierra Nevada, is tall and erect, and has fairly large, upturned, whitish petals. Although it occurs near *reflexa*, it flowers a month later. There are at least two ecological races within this subspecies.

The high-altitude subspecies *nevadensis* is very sparsely pubescent, has large, showy, expanded, whitish petals and long, slender rhizomes, whereas the other three subspecies have branched, woody crowns. Subspecies *nevadensis* includes both a subalpine and an alpine ecological race, and the change from one race to another takes place at approximately the same altitude as in *Achillea*. Unlike the latter, however, *Potentilla glandulosa* has not produced any races for the Great Basin plateau.

The Coast Range forms of subspecies *typica* grow tallest at Stanford and decrease in size at Mather (fig. 17), whereas the forms of *reflexa* grow most vigorously at Mather, where they are native. Both die when transplanted to the alpine garden. Subspecies *Hanseni* remains strongly winter-dormant when transplanted to Stanford and it produces few flowers there. It is the tallest race at Mather, and survives at the alpine station, although it seldom is able to set ripe seed at this high altitude. *Nevadensis* is the only subspecies that consistently is able to mature its seed at Timberline. Its forms are most vigorous at Mather, however. At Stanford they retain their winter dormancy, which is shortened to two or three months, but they are very weak when they emerge in mid-March, and are just barely able to survive at the lowland station.

We find, therefore, that in *Potentilla glandulosa* the variability is compartmentalized within four morphologically recognizable geographic subspecies, that these subspecies are also ecologically different, but that each of them contains two or more ecological races. Some of the ecological races change in the same altitudinal ranges as corresponding races of *Achillea,* and others at slightly different altitudes. The subspecies of *Potentilla glandulosa* have no barriers to interbreeding except those provided by the ecological separation. At mid-altitudes two subspecies, *reflexa* and *Hanseni,* occur in the same region but are separated edaphically, the former occurring on dry slopes, the latter in moist meadows. Their relative isolation is further enhanced by a difference in the time of flowering. Natural hybrids occur where the two subspecies are adjacent, but the hybrids do not obscure the distinctness of the subspecies. Interestingly enough, in 7 populations of *reflexa* and 10 of *Hanseni* which were grown in the Stanford garden, no evidence was found of intermixture by migration of genes away from the points of contact of the two subspecies.

The Madiinae— The California tarweeds constitute a subtribe of the sunflower family with approximately 75 species distributed in about 10 genera. These plants are annuals and occupy mainly the

Coast Ranges and the foothills of California. Accordingly, they have fewer ecological races than do the perennials that occupy different climatic zones up to the top of the mountains. The *Madiinae* seem to have specialized in evolving species and genera rather than ecologic races, so that they have been able to accumulate a greater number of evolutionary entities in a given area than have groups of plants that maintain their variability in the form of ecological races within one species. Also, because the *Madiinae* are annuals, their vernal forms can escape the warm and dry summers characteristic of the winter rain regions by surviving as seeds.

Fig. 18. Parallel maritime races in two species of *Layia. Left to right: Layia platyglossa* originally from Point Joe, Monterey Peninsula, California, and from south of Jenner, Sonoma County, and *L. chrysanthemoides* from the same maritime locality as the latter. All three plants grown in the Carnegie Institution greenhouse at Stanford.

Such is the case with the species of the genus *Layia,* which are spring-flowering annuals that complete their annual life cycle before June. Two *Layia* species, *platyglossa* (F. et M.) Gray and *chrysanthemoides* (DC.) Gray, extend to the coastal bluffs, where both species have evolved maritime races which are prostrate in habit, thick-stemmed, and late-flowering. These species are genetically so different that they barely are able to cross with each other, but both have evolved maritime and inland races that mimic each other. Figure 18 shows one maritime race of *chrysanthemoides* and individuals of two populations of the maritime race of *platyglossa,* the latter two about 180 miles apart. The northernmost population of *platyglossa*

49

grew within 100 feet of the maritime population of *chrysanthemoides*.

Other species of the *Madiinae* have not been able to evolve quite as specialized maritime races as have the Layias. In the genus *Hemizonia* some species have eliminated the central leader of flowering stem and produce plants with short, spreading branches originating from the crown. Other *Hemizonia* species that reached the immediate coast kept the central leader but shortened the internodes or developed horizontal side branches. Each group of species seems to evolve fitness to an exposed maritime habitat in a somewhat different way.

Seasonal ecotypes— At lower altitudes in California the growth season is very long, and climatically the autumn season is much drier than is the spring season. Some species of the *Madiinae* have succeeded in evolving races that have very different seasonal periodicities in the same locality. One of the best examples is found in *Madia elegans* Don, which at low altitude has both a spring- and a fall-flowering race. The spring form of this annual species develops no rosette leaves, but flowers quickly in March to May and withers after its seeds are ripe. The fall-flowering form, on the other hand, requires the entire spring to develop a dense basal rosette of leaves and a long taproot, and does not form flowering stems until warm summer days set in. Its giant stems are elaborately clothed with leaves, and both the leaves and stems are extremely glandular, in contrast with the almost nonglandular spring race. The most extreme fall forms do not begin their flowering before August, two months after the spring form has dried up. Figure 19 shows a row each of a spring- and fall-flowering race in the Stanford garden, the former almost dried up, the latter in very first flower.

Kinds of ecological races— Three major sets of factors in the environment have been decisive in the development of ecological races, namely, climate, soils, and other organisms. All of these three are interrelated and contribute to natural selection, but climatic, edaphic, or biotic ecotypes can be recognized, depending upon which of these sets of factors has been relatively the most dominant. The two mid-altitude races of *Potentilla glandulosa,* for example, are both climatic and edaphic. Distinctive races of several species having different degrees of tolerance to serpentine calcium-deficient soils

Fig. 19. Seasonal races in *Madia elegans. Left,* a row of a tall fall-blooming race from Putah Creek, Napa County, California, just starting to flower; *right,* a spring-blooming race almost past flowering.

have been found in California by Kruckeberg (1951). The best-known example of biotic races is in the flaxweed *Camelina sativa,* described by Tedin (1925) and by Sinskaia and Beztuzheva (1930–

1931). Its races correspond in habit, in period of seasonal development, and in seed size to the races of flax and other crops among which it grows, and obviously have been selected unintentionally by man through his agricultural operations. Superimposed on this biotic selection in *Camelina* is a climatic one, because races from northern and southern Russia show latitudinal differences that correspond with climatic differences in season and rainfall.

The dynamics of ecological races— The selective processes that lead to the development of the ecological races are not rigid. Many compromises are tolerated, and the fitness of a particular plant depends not so much upon a single character as upon a combination of several. Such a compensatory system is flexible, for a relative lack of fitness in one character may be compensated by special suitability in another. In each environment those plants have survived that are in rhythm with the diurnal and seasonal periodicities of the habitat, that can tolerate the moisture and wind conditions, that can utilize the soil there, and that can compete with other plants and animals. It is seldom that there is perfect fitness or balance to all of these conditions.

Interpopulation and interrace exchange of genes takes place in a group of plants where the individual populations are near enough to each other for occasional intermixture of pollen and seeds. The new combinations may or may not survive, depending upon their genetic make-up and their range of physiological tolerance. The survivors interbreed with other biotypes in the population and contribute to the richness of its genetic variation. Meanwhile, the environment constantly eliminates unfit variants and in this manner acts as a sifting screen, but the sifting of the various environments differs, and ecologically different races or ecotypes result.

The equilibrium between the race and its environment is maintained through the potential genetic variation within the race, which is balanced against the selecting activity of the factors of the environment. Such an equilibrium is somewhat buffered, permitting changes in the genetic composition of the race to follow changes in the environment. The ecological race maintains such flexibility so long as it maintains its actual and potential morphological and physiological diversity. The inherited diversity provides it with means of adjusting to changing conditions and assures the continuity of the species, even though the composition of its races may change in the process.

The ecological races within a species are less stable than the species as a whole because they can freely exchange their genes. Thus the inherent variability is fairly fluid. The races within a species can probably evolve relatively quickly in rapidly changing environments, and it is possible that it requires only a few generations to develop a new ecological race or to change an old one to fit new conditions.

V

The Genetic Systems of Ecological Races and Morphological Subspecies

THE characteristics of climatic races and other evolutionary entities below the species level are inherited and are therefore determined by genes, the submicroscopic carriers of heredity located in the chromosomes of living things. Evidence shows that each characteristic, like habit of growth, time of flowering, resistance to frost, dormancy, and so on, is usually regulated by several genes, each of which produces a minor effect. The effects of several genes of this kind may be added together, producing a noticeable difference. Genes of such additive effect are called multiple genes. It is not uncommon to find systems of multiple genes of opposite effect balanced against each other.

Genes probably operate through the agency of enzymes, hormones, and physiological processes, whereby they produce their growth effect and other responses. In fact, we do not know how many steps intervene between the gene and the expression of the character it regulates. The genes composing the genetic systems of ecological races and morphological subspecies are often linked into systems that determine the essential characteristics of our basic evolutionary entities. The chromosomes that carry the genes and the chromosome sets that contain the basic hereditary elements of the species provide the physical means for the development of such genetic systems.

The genes which geneticists in the early period of Mendelism selected for study in exploring the laws of heredity were those that had a major effect on the organism. Their effect on the offspring resulting from crossings could be recognized without difficulty. The kind of genes that distinguish races of wild plants are of the multiple type, and the segregating progeny which occur after crossing such races are usually difficult to classify. Consequently, wild forms have been studied less frequently by geneticists than have cultivated plants of simpler genetic composition. Our present knowledge of the genetic systems of wild forms is therefore very limited. In the following pages we shall discuss a few examples of genetic systems of wild races and subspecies, beginning with one of the simplest cases.

Fig. 20. Viola tricolor. Left, the horizontal, maritime race after three generations of inbreeding. *Right,* a segregated erect form. (From Clausen, 1926.)

Viola tricolor, the wild pansy— In Chapter III it was mentioned that on the west coast of Jutland, Denmark, which is exposed to the heavy wind from the North Sea, there is a maritime race of the wild pansy which has horizontal purple stems, is perennial, and has small, succulent leaves. It intercrosses freely with an erect inland form that grows adjacent to it, and the fertile hybrid produces in the second generation a varied array of offspring.

When the prostrate form from the maritime dunes is crossed with the erect inland form, the first-generation hybrid is found to be nearly prostrate (Clausen, 1926). In the second generation, 1 among 16 is as erect as the inland parent. The difference between the two lies in the central leader or stem, which is erect in the inland form and horizontal in the maritime. Figure 20 shows this difference between the maritime parent type and a segregated erect plant. The erect plants orient themselves rather quickly if they are disturbed. For example, when erect plants are forcibly held down horizontally in the field by placing rocks on the main stems, keeping the tips free, the growing stem ends bend upward into the vertical position again within less than a day.

The segregations for habit of growth in three different crossings between maritime and inland races of *Viola tricolor* L. are given below in table 1. The theoretical frequencies and the ratios listed are

Table 1. Segregation in stem habits in *Viola tricolor*.

	Observed no. of individuals	Theoretical frequency	Ratio
In F_2, maritime $\times$ inland races (total from 3 different crossings):			
Stem horizontal or nearly so	1876	1905.0	15
Stem fully erect	156	127.0	1
In F_3, from 1 selfed horizontal plant:			
Stem horizontal	126	124.5	3
Stem erect	40	41.5	1
In F_4, from 3 selfed erect plants:			
Stem erect	104, 56, 27		
(none horizontal)			

based on the assumption that the maritime race has two fairly dominant pairs of genes which cause the central stem to be horizontal.

The 3 : 1 ratio in the F_3 offspring of a horizontal F_2 plant proves that only one gene is really needed to make the stems mostly horizontal. In the maritime race, however, there are four genes for horizontal habit, and such plants are horizontal under all conditions, whereas those with only one to three genes are horizontal in full sun only and tend to become ascending or erect in partial shade.

The dune race differs also from the inland race by having a darker, purplish stem, a character determined by two pairs of genes. These two are of the truly multiple type, as evidenced by the fact that the F_1 is intermediate and that all shades of purple exist in the second generation. Only those individuals that possess a full set of four, or two pairs, of these genes are fully purple. Another series of genes is responsible for the perennial habit in the dune race. The perennial form develops many side shoots from the root crown during autumn, but the annual inland form at that time dries up and dies. The F_1 hybrid between the two is fairly perennial, the annuals are segregated again in the F_2, but there are too many transitional types to make possible a clear classification into annuals and perennials.

Other characteristics of the maritime race include an acuminate tip on the lower petal that is lacking on the inland form and small, succulent leaves in contrast with the larger and thinner leaves of the inland form. Figure 21 shows these differences in the flowers and leaves of the maritime and inland parents (21 *a* and *c,* respectively) and in the F_1 hybrid (21 *b*). The segregations in the F_2 are fairly complex for these characters, although the F_1 has leaves that are as large as those of its inland parent. One F_2 population in which classification of acuminate tip was attempted provided a graded series of 300 individuals with more or less pointed lower petals to 205 without such a tip. Such a complex segregation suggests the interplay of more than one pair of genes.

An estimate indicates that a minimum of 15 to 20 pairs of genes are responsible for the principal morphological differences that distinguish the maritime and the inland races of *Viola tricolor* from each other. No genetic linkages between characters were observed in this species, but it has 13 pairs of chromosomes, a number that is high enough to permit a wide degree of freedom in the distribution of the genes to different chromosomes.

Viola tricolor is very variable in flower color, and in hybrid progeny the segregation of various patterns of petal color are more clear-cut and easier to classify than the segregations for ecologically important differences associated with the maritime and the inland habitats. A surprisingly large number of genes govern the colors in the five petals of the wild pansy. Velvety black is the bottom recessive of these, and the common wild-type pansy, which has violet petals, differs from black by possessing five pairs of dominant and epistatic (covering) pairs of genes which modify the black color step by step by removing its velvety character from various parts of the petals

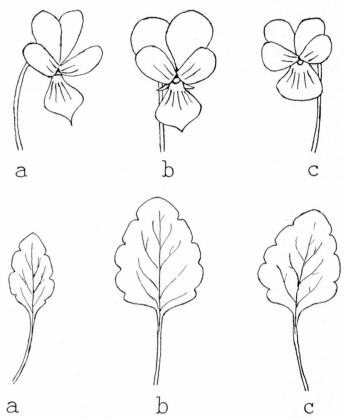

Fig. 21. Flowers and leaves of *Viola tricolor: a,* maritime dune race; *c,* inland race; *b,* the F_1 hybrid. (From Clausen, 1926.)

(Clausen, 1926, 1930). The further addition of a pair of genes will change the violet of the wild type to the less common deep yellow, whereas a recessive pair of genes changes violet to rose pink. Finally, very rarely there are plants in the wild with completely white petals and no trace of purple in the stems. These are recessive for a series of genes basic for the development of violet, but not of yellow color.

Most wild-type forms of *Viola tricolor* possess two pairs of the basic genes for violet, but some have three pairs, although the presence of only a single one of the basic genes is sufficient for full development of the violet color. The major patterns in flower color of *Viola tricolor* are therefore determined by the interaction of a series of 9 to 10 pairs of genes, the darkest color being the most recessive.

Even relatively insignificant characteristics are determined by such complex gene systems. Many strains of the wild pansies have an inconspicuous dark mark on the front of the pistil, pointing toward the honey glands within the base of the spur. This character is governed by a series of genes pulling in opposite directions. The presence of pistil spot is far more common than is its absence in normally cross-pollinated *Viola tricolor,* and it is inherited as a dominant character in ratios of either $3 : 1$ or $9 : 7$. There are apparently positive genes for spot having different strengths, some requiring the presence of a complementary gene and others not. In the closely related but self-pollinated *Viola arvensis,* however, absence of spot is the most common situation, and presence of spot is generally inherited as a recessive. Many *arvensis* strains possess the gene for spot, but it does not come to expression because it is suppressed by one or two inhibitors. When, in a cross between forms with and without spot, both parents have the positive gene for spot but the one without spot has the inhibitors, then the F_1 is without spot and the F_2 may segregate according to ratios $3 : 1$ or $9 : 7$, with nonspot as the most frequent type. If the nonspot parent possesses the two complementary suppressors for spot but not the positive gene for spot itself, then the F_1 will also be without spot, but the F_2 will segregate in the ratio of $43 : 21$, with spot as the recessive type. However, some of the supposedly recessive plants with spot will turn the tables and in the F_3 segregate nonspot as a recessive in the ratio $3 : 1$. This rather intricate system of genes of opposing effect contributes to an elusiveness in the inheritance of this minute character, but such a system is generally found in wild races of other families. Examples that have long been on record include the inheritance of density of ears in wheat and of seed color in corn.

A question sometimes asked is what would happen if a maritime race was grown for many generations in an inland environment. The implication of this question is that the impact of the inland environment through many generations would finally change the maritime to the inland race. Nobody has as yet had time to grow a thousand generations of a plant since the time of Lamarck, but some information relating to this subject is on hand in the case of the maritime race of *Viola tricolor*.

The maritime race of *Viola tricolor* is fairly self-incompatible and suffers by continuous inbreeding. After three or four generations of selfing it is so weak that it can barely be kept alive. All the inland forms of that species, however, are self-compatible and will stand selfing indefinitely without loss of vigor, although normally they are cross-pollinated.

When the maritime race was lost as the result of too much selfing, a new one was synthesized from a cross between an inland and the maritime form by selecting among the segregants. The new product had the maritime characteristics of long, completely horizontal, dark-purplish stems, narrow, pointed petals, small, succulent leaves, and the habit of producing many new shoots from the root crown in the fall, making it moderately perennial. The only morphological character it had inherited from the inland parent was velvety upper petals, but it had also obtained the physiological character of ability to tolerate selfing without loss of vigor. In all other respects the synthesized maritime was indistinguishable from the natural one.

Seeds of the original maritime race were taken in 1919 in a dune habitat west of Skagen, Denmark. This race was grown for four generations inland, near Lyngby, Sjaelland, 150 miles removed from the boisterous maritime habitat of its progenitor on the northern sandspit of Denmark, but by the third generation it was so much weakened by inbreeding that it was very difficult to obtain seed on it. Pollen of the third generation of the maritime grown at Lyngby was used in crossing an inland race in 1923. A good new synthetic maritime form had appeared already in the F_2 in 1925, but it did not become genetically constant before the F_5 generation in 1928, which was grown at Berkeley, California. The new strain was brought back to Lyngby, Denmark, in 1928 and this stabilized form was grown there yearly until 1931. It was brought back to California and sown at Stanford in 1932 in a garden well protected from the sea by a mountain range and was grown here for two generations, up to the F_8 from the crossing. Eleven generations removed from its maritime habitat, it was in 1933 given to Professor Milo S. Baker of Santa Rosa Junior College, who grew it in his *Viola* garden in a protected inland environment at Kenwood, Sonoma County, California, until 1940. It sowed itself in this garden but maintained all of its characteristic features, and it was still as typically maritime as its progenitors on the North Sea dune.

This case, not previously reported, is one of the best examples of the persistence of the heredity of an ecological race against drastic changes in an environment through many generations over a period of twenty years and on two continents. Possibly the most severe test of the constancy of the heredity of the maritime race was sending its genes through the germ plasm of the contrasting inland race and recovering the maritime form again.

Races of Layia— It was mentioned that two species of the California *Layia* or tidytips of the *Madiinae* have developed parallel maritime races where they occur together at exposed coasts. The maritime race of *Layia platyglossa* occurs in isolated colonies over a distance of nearly 300 miles along the immediate coast of central California. Five crossings between maritime and inland populations of *Layia platyglossa* were made which produced some 3600 F_2's and 2700 F_3's.

The data from the segregations in the second generations of these various hybrids between maritime and inland races indicate that different sets of genes operate in different crosses, for the ratios of the corresponding segregated phenotypes are often reversed, although the same kinds of types are segregated in all of the crosses.

Three of the ecologically most important differences between the maritime and inland races of *Layia* seem to be horizontal versus erect habit, absence or presence of a central leader, and late versus early flowering, respectively. The first two of these differences can be studied from figure 22, which shows an individual of each of the two races, with their F_1 hybrid. The F_1's between various populations of these two races differ slightly, ranging from decumbent to horizontal branching and from the presence of a short central leader to none at all. All the hybrids are fairly early in flowering and are fully fertile (Clausen, Keck, and Hiesey, 1947).

The second generations of such racial crosses are all very variable. They segregate for growth habit and recombine the parental characteristics in typical Mendelian fashion, as suggested in figure 23.

Fig. 22. *Layia platyglossa*. *Left,* maritime race from Point Joe, Monterey Peninsula, California; *right,* inland race from near Jolon; *center,* the F_1 hybrid. (From Clausen, Keck, and Hiesey, 1947.)

The growth habits of the parental types are shown in the upper left and lower right corners, respectively. Some of the offspring recombine the parental characteristics to produce new types, as, for example, some that combine the horizontal branches of the maritime race with the presence of the central leader of the inland form (23 *b*), and others that combine the absence of leader, a maritime characteristic, with the erect branches of the inland race (23 *e*). Almost perfectly intergrading series of phenotypes between the parental extremes occur in such racial segregations, a situation that makes the classification of the intermediate classes uncertain, although the extreme parental types for each character can be recognized.

The F_2 segregations in *Layia platyglossa* for the three characters of central leader, type of branching, and earliness of flowering are summarized in table 2 for three of the interracial hybrids in order to show both the Mendelian ratios that most closely fit and the correlations between characters of the original parental combinations shown in the upper left and lower right corners of each division of the table.

Table 2. *Layia platyglossa,* maritime × inland race; segregations in F_2 for three characters.

	Cambria × Pala				Jenner × Bernardino				Pt. Joe × Etiwanda			
	Earliness		Total	Ra-tio	*Earliness*		Total	Ra-tio	*Earliness*		Total	Ra-tio
	late	early			late	early			late	early		
Central leader:												
none	28	177	205	1	173	679	852	—	14	462	476	9
present	11	609	620	3	32	437	459	—	2	325	327	7
Branching:												
horizontal ascending	39	461	500	9	96	122	218	3	10	59	69	1
to erect	—	325	325	7	109	994	1103	13	6	728	734	15
Total	39	786	825	16	205	1116	1321	16	16	787	803	16
Ratio	1	15	16		3	13	16		1	63	64	

It will be seen that the ratios vary between 3 : 1, 15 : 1, 63 : 1, 9 : 7, and 13 : 3. Such ratios first suggest that for any one of these characters the parents may differ by at least one to three pairs of genes. Some of these ratios, namely, 15 : 1 and 63 : 1, indicate that genes of the multiple type are responsible; others, like 9 : 7, that the genes are complementary, requiring that both genes be present in order to produce their effect; the 13 : 3 ratio suggests the action both of a gene with positive effect and of another gene inhibiting it.

For any one character the ratios vary from one cross to the next. The presence of central leader, for example, is dominant in one cross, recessive in another, and inhibited by two complementary genes in a third, indicating that the genetic basis is more complicated than the individual ratios would suggest. The intergrading observed between the extremes supports the conclusion that probably even more genes are involved. The inheritance of the mode of branching shows similar apparent shifts in the ratios, indicating complexity in gene action. The genetic mechanism distinguishing maritime and inland races of *Layia* of the sunflower family therefore is very similar to that of corresponding races of the wild pansies of the violet family.

The various genes governing different characters are linked to-

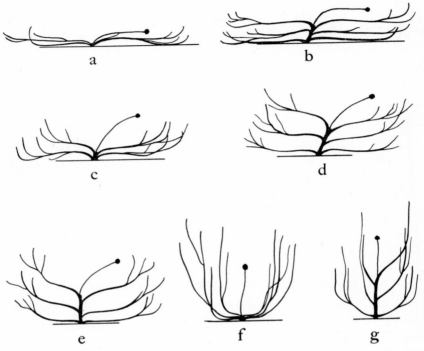

Fig. 23. Segregation in growth habit in the F_2 of maritime $\times$ inland races of *Layia platyglossa. Upper left,* the parental, prostrate maritime type; *lower right,* the erect inland type. (After Clausen, Keck, and Hiesey, 1947.)

gether in *Layia* so that in the second-generation offspring of the crosses the parental maritime and inland types reappear with considerably greater frequency than would otherwise be expected if the distribution of the controlling genes had been strictly at random. In each of the six subdivisions of table 2, the upper left and the lower right groups of individuals are greater than they should be if purely random segregation had taken place. Although we as yet do not know the details of the genetic structure that controls these ecological races, it is obvious that they possess a mechanism that favors the reappearance of the parental combinations when the races are crossed. This mechanism is probably genetic linkage, which in *Layia* would be favored because of the low number of chromosomes, $n = 7$, in this species. In *Viola tricolor* with $n = 13$ chromosomes, such genetic linkages were not so apparent.

Some genes govern the direction of the central peduncle (fig. 23), others govern the length of the internodes between the branches, and still others the succulence of the leaves and stems in the maritime race. It is evident, therefore, that even neighboring ecological races of one species differ from each other in a considerable number of genes.

The prostrate maritime populations of *Layia platyglossa* are found in scattered colonies along the coast of California over a distance of more than 300 miles. The question arises as to whether the distinguishing characters of the maritime populations represent independent parallel selections from local inland types or whether they are genetically a single interconnected racial complex. Two maritime populations coming from 140 miles apart and also separated by San Francisco Bay were intercrossed. These were from south of Jenner, Sonoma County, and from Point Joe, on the Monterey Peninsula, both of which are shown to the left in figure 18, p. 49. The F_1 of this cross was prostrate, and not a single early-flowering individual of erect habit was segregated among more than 1400 second-generation plants of this cross. They were all of the late-flowering, succulent, horizontal type without central leader. In other respects, such as density of internodes and number of disk and ray florets, this F_2 was very variable. Likewise, none of the various populations of the erect inland form produced any plants of the prostrate, maritime type when crossed among themselves. It is accordingly concluded that the many genes that determine the characteristics of these two races are identically arranged in the chromosomes. The identical arrangement might mean that the maritime race has arisen only once, or it might have come about because the chromosomes of the species are so constituted that series of independent mutations of the same kind can arise independently in the same loci of the chromosomes in individuals at remote geographical localities and at different times. A third, more plausible, possibility exists, namely, that the maritime race is the original one of the species and that it existed on the bluffs of the Pacific shore line even before the Golden Gate channel was as wide as it is now.

The maritime race of *Layia platyglossa* (Fisch. et Mey.) Gray was the first race of the species collected by botanists in the former Russian colony on the west coast of California north of present San Francisco. The seeds were sent to Russia and the species was described in 1849 by Fischer and Meyer from plants grown in the Botanical Garden of St. Petersburg, Russia. A few years later the species was grown at Kew Gardens, England, from seeds obtained from St. Petersburg, and herbarium specimens were taken which still are in the Kew Herbarium. These plants are clearly of the maritime race, although they are several generations removed from those on the California coast, and were grown in England. They developed there the succulent, horizontal stems without central leader and had the broad and flat bracts on the peduncle which gave the species its name and which even today are characteristic of the population from south of Jenner in the vicinity of the type locality. Experiences like this one suggest that the local population and the ecological race may remain relatively unchanged at the same spot for many years.

The complicated genetic structure of natural populations can be illustrated by the inheritance of interlaced hairs on the pappus of the akenes of some of the forms of *Layia platyglossa* from southern California. The difference between floccose (cottony) and nonfloccose pappus was originally made the basis of two distinct species, but it will be recalled from Chapter III that these two forms occur together in almost every population south of the San Bernardino Mountains. The floccose form was named *Madaroglossa elegans* Nutt. North of the San Bernardinos all populations are nonfloccose. The nonfloccose plants from the areas south and north of the San Bernardinos are, however, genetically different, the former being dominant and the latter fairly recessive in relation to the floccose character. This difference in dominance can be seen in figure 24. In the left half of this figure at 24 *a* is an akene from a nonfloccose population from the San Bernardino Plains, and at *c* one from a floccose colony from the nearby mesa of Etiwanda. In the center at *b* is an akene of their F_1 hybrid, which shows the dominance of the nonfloccose character. The right half of figure 24 shows at *d* an akene typical of the Point Joe population from the Monterey Peninsula, which, like all northern populations, has nonfloccose pappus; on the right at *f* is again the fully floccose akene of the Etiwanda form, and, in the center at *e,* an akene of their F_1 hybrid with partially floccose pappus, which is very different from the F_1 below. These facts and the segregations in the F_2's are summarized in table 3.

Table 3. Layia platyglossa, inheritance of floccose pappus.

F₁ segregations	San Bernardino × Etiwanda nonfloccose			Point Joe × Etiwanda partially floccose			Cambria × Pala partially floccose		
F₂ segregations	No. of individuals	Theoretical	Ratio	No. of individuals	Theoretical	Ratio	No. of individuals	Theoretical	Ratio
nonfloccose	725	701.3	13	25	25.1	1	63	51.5	1
trace	—	—	—	141	175.7	7	109	103.0	2
medium to fully floccose	138	161.7	3	648	602.2	24	653	670.5	13
Total	863	863	16	803	803	32	825	825	16

The simplest explanation of the difference in degree of dominance and also of the observed segregations in the F_2 is that cottony pappus can be suppressed by the presence of a single dominant gene of the nonfloccose plants from the south, whereas the suppressor genes in the populations from north of the San Bernardinos are weaker, so that it takes two to three pairs of them to suppress the cotton fully. The 13 : 3 ratio in the San Bernardino × Etiwanda cross indicates that there is probably also a positive gene for floccose pappus. The Etiwanda parent has this gene but not its suppressor, whereas the San Bernardino parent has the suppressor for the floccose pappus but not the positive gene for it. Such complex segregations are apparently the result of the interplay between genes of opposite effect, as in the example of the black spot in front of the pistil of the violets.

One of the suppressors in the populations north of the San Bernardinos appears to be much stronger than the others, as witnessed by the fairly large number of plants with only a trace of cotton. Also, the Point Joe population has three pairs of suppressor genes, because one of the two F_1 individuals which produced the F_2 by mutual pollination was heterozygous for three, and the other for only two pairs of these genes, resulting in a segregation of $24 : 7 : 1$ in the F_2. The Cambria population, on the other hand, seemed to have only two pairs of suppressors. The classification for nonfloccose is clear-

Fig. 24. Inheritance of pappus character in *Layia platyglossa*. *Left half, a,* nonfloccose form from San Bernardino; *c,* floccose type from Etiwanda; *b,* their nonfloccose F_1 hybrid. *Right half, d,* nonfloccose from Point Joe; *f,* floccose from Etiwanda; *e,* their partially floccose F_1.

cut, whereas a long series of intergrades ranging from "trace" to fully floccose cannot be separated.

Other differences between the northern and southern populations of *Layia platyglossa* are two pairs of genes for the lemon-chrome base of the ray florets in the northern, as against the lemon yellow of the southern, population and three pairs of genes that determine the difference between the black anthers of the north and the yellow ones of the south.

Layia chrysanthemoides (DC.) Gray is another 7-chromosome species that reaches the coast. South of Jenner, at a point about 30 miles north of San Francisco, a maritime form of *Layia platyglossa* is found on exposed bluffs on one side of the coast highway and on the other side is found the equally prostrate, late-flowering maritime race of *Layia chrysanthemoides*. Superficially the two maritime races resemble each other, as was indicated in figure 18, p. 49, although it is almost impossible to intercross the two very different species.

The maritime and inland races of *Layia chrysanthemoides* differ from each other in much the same manner as the corresponding races of *Layia platyglossa*, as shown in figure 25. The maritime form has horizontal branches, lacks a central leader, and is late-flowering,

Fig. 25. *Layia chrysanthemoides. Left,* the prostrate, late-blooming maritime race from south of Jenner, Sonoma County, California. *Right,* the erect, early-blooming inland race from south of San Francisco.

in contrast with the ascending branches, erect central leader, and early flowering of the inland form. The F_1 hybrid between the two has a very short central leader with very short internodes, has decumbent branches, and is intermediate in time of flowering. It is highly fertile, and an F_2 population of nearly 2000 individuals segregated for the contrasting parental characters, but in much simpler ratios than in *platyglossa*, as table 4 indicates.

The inland race of *chrysanthemoides* has hairy akenes with a crown of scaly pappus, as indicated in figure 26, whereas the coastal race has completely smooth, black akenes without a trace of pappus. Lack of pappus and smooth akenes are determined by the same gene and are inherited together, and the F_1 hybrid is nonpappose just like the coastal type. The segregation in the F_2 is simple, with dominance of the smooth, nonpappose type, as shown in table 4. There is some indication, however, that the dominant inhibitor for pappus and pubescence submerges the effect of weak modifying genes that usually do not come to expression, for a few individuals classified as nonpappose had faint traces of pappus and of hairs on the akenes.

Table 4. Layia chrysanthemoides, segregation in the F_2 of maritime $\times$ inland races.

	Observed no. of individuals	Theoretical frequency	Ratio
Central leader present	1676	1607.9	13
Central leader absent	303	371.1	3
Branches ascending-erect	1108	1113.1	9
Branches horizontal	871	865.9	7
Pappus absent	1518	1484.3	3
Pappus present	461	494.7	1

The difference between the akenes of the smooth and those of the pubescent and pappose form is so striking that the form with the smooth akenes was originally referred to a different genus. An interesting story not previously recorded is connected with this misinterpretation. Certain colonies of this species contain both pappose and nonpappose plants, but the two local variants look alike unless the seeds are inspected. In the late twenties of the ninteenth century the famous Scottish plant collector David Douglas collected plants and seeds of this species, at that time undescribed, somewhere in the outer Coast Range of California and sent them to the Horticultural Society in London, which, in turn, referred the plants to De Candolle in Geneva for determination. De Candolle received the plant without pappus and described it as a new genus, *Oxyura chrysanthemoides.* Seeds of the new genus were sent to various botanical gardens in exchange, but these seeds happened to come from plants with pappus, and this caused much trouble. A note on an herbarium sheet in the Kew Herbarium, made in Luxembourg in 1839 from plants grown in the botanical garden there, states that this is a different genus and not *Oxyura;* notes on a sheet from the St. Petersburg garden in

Russia state the same. At the Horticultural Society a color plate of the new species, *Oxyura chrysanthemoides,* was being prepared for publication in the Botanical Register in 1836 (tab. 1850), and the artist evidently also had the plant with pappus, which he conscientiously illustrated. When the botanist who wrote the text accompanying the plate came to describe the pappus, he accused the artist of having made an error and having depicted the akene of another species. A few years later the pappose plant was described as *Calli-*

Fig. 26. Inheritance in akene character in *Layia chrysanthemoides. Left,* pubescent and pappose akene of the recessive *Calliglossa* form; *right,* the genetically dominant form with smooth, non-pappose akenes of the type of the species; *center,* the smooth, nonpappose akene of the F_1 hybrid.

glossa Hook. et Arn. Nobody had discovered that several of the herbarium sheets in Douglas' original collections contained plants of both "genera." It is now clear that these striking forms are only local genetic variants of one species, *Layia chrysanthemoides,* differing by only one pair of genes. The pappose form, which is recessive, could have originated from the nonpappose one on the windy maritime bluffs by a simple loss of the inhibiting gene, and the winds would tend to blow the mutant inland.

The parental characteristics of races of *Layia chrysanthemoides* are also linked, suggesting that the genes for several characters may be located in the same chromosomes. Such parallelism suggests similarity in the genetic history of the species *chrysanthemoides* and *platyglossa,* although the chromosomes of the two are only partially homologous.

Madia elegans, seasonal ecotypes— It was mentioned in Chapter IV that *Madia elegans* Don, an 8-chromosome tall annual of the *Madiinae,* possesses ecological races that are adapted to different seasons of the year. Geographically, the spring- and fall-flowering races may therefore occur together, although they flower in different seasons of the year and the former may have withered before the latter begins to bloom. A spring-flowering race from the foothills of the Sierra Nevada was crossed with a giant, fall-flowering form from the inner Coast Range. They are shown growing in the Stanford garden in figure 19, page 51. The spring race flowers in May, has few but large leaves with few glands, and varies in height between 45 and 75 cm., whereas the fall race flowers in August, develops its stems during the hot summer, is densely covered by leaves and glands, and towers between 75 and 207 cm. Figure 27 depicts the variation in height and the difference in earliness between the parental races, the F_1, and the F_2. The first-generation hybrid between the spring- and fall-flowering races is intermediate in most respects, although it blooms about June 1, only a little later than the spring parent. Of the 1135 F_2's, nearly three-fourths flowered in May like the spring parent, and only 16 came into bloom during the period from July 9 to August 1. This result would indicate that there is one dominant gene for early flowering, which, when present, covers the effect of at least three pairs of genes for late flowering. This situation is interpreted to mean that the time of flowering is determined by a series of genes which pull in different directions.

Other genes were responsible for the difference in the architecture of the plants, in the glands, leaves, and height. The heights of the 1135 F_2 plants varied between 10 and 205 cm., the latter being the maximum height for the fall-flowering race. The genes that determine late flowering and tall growth are strongly linked, for the 16 plants that were the latest to flower included also the 11 tallest plants.

Altitudinal races in Potentilla glandulosa— It was mentioned in Chapter IV that *Potentilla glandulosa,* a species with only 7 pairs of chromosomes, has developed subspecies that are morphologically distinct but of ecotypic nature, because they occupy zones of different

Height cm.	Numbers of Individuals			
	Clarksville	Putah Ck.	F$_1$	F$_2$
210	·	2	·	
200	·	2	·	1
190	·	7	·	3 late
180	·	4	·	4 flowering
170	·	9	·	3
160	·	10	·	5
150	·	9	·	14
140	·	8	·	31
130	·	12	2	35
120	·	10	3	69
110	·	8	4	76
100	·	5	1	109
90	·	9	5	157
80	·	2	1	167
70	3	2	·	117
60	13	·	·	105
50	11	·	·	83
40	3	·	·	41
30	3	·	·	39
20	·	·	·	27
10	·	·	·	32
0	·	·	·	17
Total	33	97	16	1135
First flowers	May	August	ca. June 1	Ratio: May:796 } 1116 63 Jun.1–Jul.8:323 } Jul.9–Aug.1: 16 16 1

Fig. 27. Inheritance of height and earliness of blooming in a cross between a spring-blooming race, *vernalis,* and a fall-blooming race, *autumnalis,* of *Madia elegans.*

environment. Nevertheless, each subspecies contains more than one ecological race.

Hybrids between the subspecies of *Potentilla* are vigorous and fertile. One of these was a cross between a race of subspecies *typica* from the mild coast and a race of subspecies *nevadensis* from a severe alpine climate at 11,000 feet in the Sierra Nevada (Clausen, Keck, and Hiesey, 1940; Clausen, 1949). The F_1 was very fertile, and a second generation of approximately 1000 individuals was grown at Stanford. In figure 28 are shown the parental forms, the F_1, and a small sample of the variation in the F_2, which shows the great variability in the offspring of a hybrid between races so different. The segregation of about 15 characters was analyzed. Each character was found to be governed by more than one pair of genes. The coastal parent is winter-active in the mild Stanford environment, the alpine is dormant, and F_1 is intermediate. Several individuals of the second generation are as winter-active as the coastal parent, having new leaves about 15 cm. long in mid-January, and others are fully dormant like the alpine parent, with a long series of intergrades connecting them.

Another hybrid between the foothill race and the subalpine race from 10,000 feet produced a second generation of 575 plants, which segregated as thoroughly as in the former cross. These were cloned and planted in the transplant gardens at 100-foot, 4600-foot, and 10,000-foot altitudes, and the responses for 16 different characters were studied for a period of 7 to 9 years. These studies included characters such as color, length and width of petals, color of stems, size and color of seeds, height, number of stems, earliness of flowering, frost resistance, and survival at the contrasting stations. Each of these characters is determined by series of genes, although usually only by 2 to 4 pairs per character. In some cases the character is determined by a series of multiple genes, each with equal effect, but in other cases one gene outweighs the others, which then function as modifiers. In still other cases the character is governed by a combination of genes with positive effect counterbalanced by inhibitors. The color of the petals, which is deep yellow in one parent and whitish in the other, depends upon the interplay between two pairs

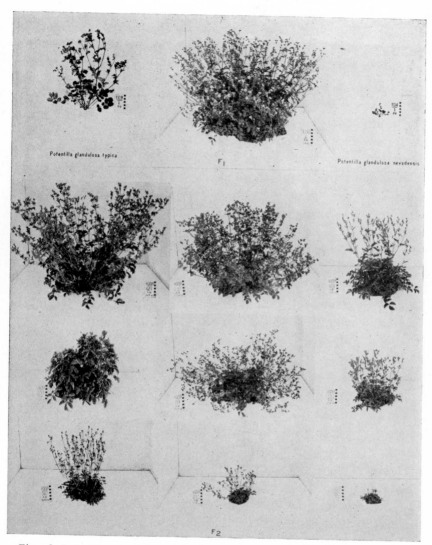

Fig. 28. Potentilla glandulosa, inheritance in a cross between a coastal and an alpine race. *Top row, left,* the coastal parent; *right,* the alpine parent; *center,* the F_1 hybrid. *Lower three rows,* samples of the F_2, showing extreme variability. All growing in the Carnegie Institution garden at Stanford. (From Clausen, 1949.)

of genes that determine the intensity of the yellow, one pair that bleaches yellow to cream, and two pairs of whitening genes super-imposed on the others. The orientation of the petals is governed by one pair of genes that bends them backwards, but the effect of this pair is covered by the presence of any one of two pairs of genes for upcurved or erect petals. These are additional examples of characters that are governed by series of genes having opposite effect. Altogether, it was estimated that as a minimum some 60 to 100 pairs of genes are responsible for the variations of those characters of *Potentilla glandulosa* that were investigated.

These genes are genetically linked together, which is to be expected in a species that has only 7 pairs of chromosomes but with climatic races having so many differences. Linkages exist between morpho-logical and physiological characteristics, such as, for example, frost resistance with notched petals. The linkages are not absolute, for individuals are segregated that morphologically favor the foothill race, but which are frost-resistant or which survive indefinitely at the alpine station.

Figure 17 (p. 46) indicates that the foothill parent dies after a very short time at the alpine station. The subalpine parent is weak at the lowland station, but the F_1 survives at all three altitudes. Consequently, the F_1 has a wider range of tolerance than either of its parents. Figure 29 shows graphs of heights of several individuals of the parental races and of the F_1 hybrid at the three transplant stations. The nonsurvival of the foothill race at the alpine station is indicated by the broken lines.

The relatively consistent patterns of response observed in the pa-rental races and in the initial hybrid disappear in the second generation after the parental genes have been exchanged. This is shown by the contrasting reactions of various cloned F_2 individuals (Clausen, Keck, and Hiesey, 1947). Figure 30 pictures the clones of three F_2 individ-uals of contrasting reactions at the transplant stations, the top one being even more alpine in its reactions than is the subalpine parent, because it is relatively the tallest at Timberline. The clone illustrated in the center of figure 30 is most vigorous at the middle altitude, but survives well at all three places, like the F_1. The bottom clone in the figure reacts like the Coast Range race, being most vigorous at Stanford. The latter plant fits an environment outside of the range of either parent.

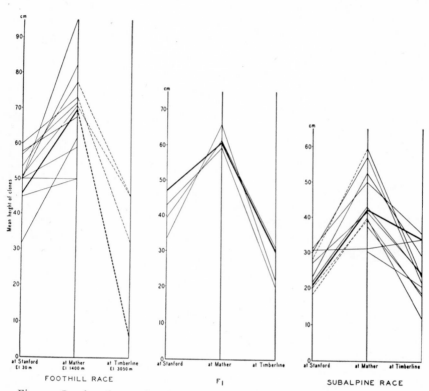

FOOTHILL RACE F_1 SUBALPINE RACE

Fig. 29. Graphs of stem heights of cloned individuals of *Potentilla glandulosa* when grown at three altitudes. *Left,* a group of twelve individuals of the foothill race. The broken lines indicate four individuals that survived one winter at Timberline but died; eight did not even survive one winter. *Right,* a group of twelve individuals of the subalpine race with poor survival at Stanford. *Center,* four F_1 hybrids of the two races, surviving at all three stations. (From Clausen, 1949.)

In figure 31 are graphed the patterns of vigor of 540 F_2 clones at the three contrasting transplant gardens. At any one station each individual was scored in relation to its vigor there, and the scores were averaged from observation over a period of from 7 to 9 years. As presented in the graph, the individuals were graded as weak,

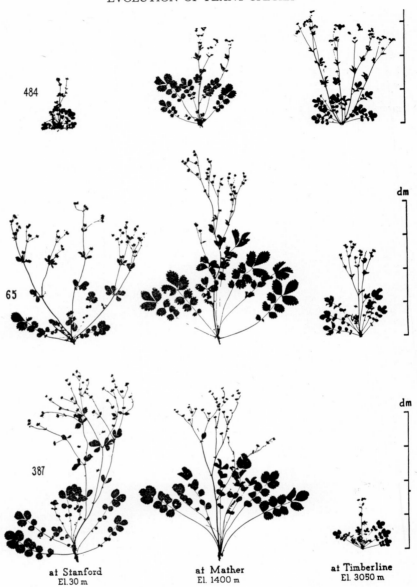

484

dm

65

dm

387

at Stanford
El. 30 m

at Mather
El. 1400 m

at Timberline
El. 3050 m

Fig. 30. Contrasting responses of three clones of the F$_2$ of the foothill $\times$ subalpine races of *Potentilla glandulosa* at the Carnegie Institution gardens at Stanford, Mather, and Timberline. *Top row,* clone 484, which is most vigorous at the alpine station. *Center row,* clone 65, which succeeds at all three stations. *Bottom row,* clone 387, which is most vigorous at Stanford. (From Clausen, Keck, and Hiesey, 1947.)

intermediate, or vigorous. To the left in this figure are graphed those individuals that were classed as weak at Stanford, in the center those that are intermediate, and to the right those that are vigorous there. The numbers on the lines indicate the total number of individuals of that combination, and the thickness of the lines shows the approximate frequency.

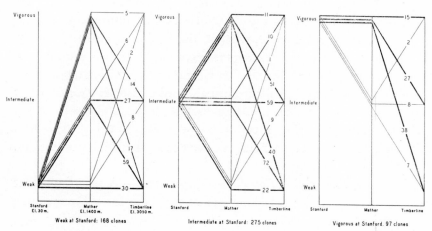

Fig. 31. Classes of growth responses in vigor in three climates of 540 cloned F_2 individuals of the cross between the foothill and subalpine races of *Potentilla glandulosa.* The clones are grouped according to their vigor at the three transplant stations. The numerals indicate the number of individuals in each group. See text. (From Clausen, 1949.)

There are groups of plants that are vigorous at either the alpine station or the mid-altitude Mather station, but are weak at Stanford. Others are more limited in their tolerance, being vigorous at the middle altitude but weak at the low and high altitudes. In contrast, there are those that are weak at Mather but of intermediate vigor at both Stanford and Timberline, and others which are vigorous at Stanford and weak at the alpine station. Some plants are poorly adapted to all three environments, although they survive, whereas others are remarkably successful at all three stations and therefore have a range of tolerance that exceeds that of any plant from the wild. Recombinations of this kind suggest the hidden evolutionary resources that can be tapped when the genes of just two individuals of contrasting races are recombined. Actually, such races contain the building blocks for many potential new ecological races.

The graph shows clearly that exchanging the genes of the ecologically very contrasting parental races has resulted in F_2 individuals of all kinds of growth patterns. Among these 540 clones, 24 of the theoretically possible 27 combinations have been realized. It is apparent that the physiological characteristics are gene-controlled, for each of the parents had a distinct and relatively uniform pattern of reaction at the three stations, whereas the F_2 displays great diversity. We see also that these characteristics express themselves as ranges of tolerance, suggesting the kinds of environment in which an individual might succeed. Crossings between such unlike climatic races as these seldom occur in the wild, but they disclose the possibilities for rapid evolution when changes in environment gradually bring such races together. The plant breeder may do well to exploit such possibilities.

The genetic structure of an evolutionary relict— A puzzling plant was discovered in 1940 in a remote sector of the dry inner Coast Range of central California (Clausen, Keck, and Hiesey, 1947). It is a tiny, spring-flowering annual, 5 to 15 cm. tall, occurring as a small colony of some 300 individuals on a hillside of unfertile serpentine soil. The plant is so unlike anything previously named that it was thought to belong to an undescribed genus. Technically it belonged to the *Helenieae,* the sneezeweed tribe of the sunflower family, but some characteristics suggested relationship to the two genera *Layia* and *Madia* of the neighboring tarweeds of *Madiinae* of the sunflower tribe. It did not fit there, however, because it had no ray florets and therefore no ray-enfolding bracts, deficiencies which technically exclude it from the tarweeds.

Some plants were removed to our experiment garden at Stanford, and others were sown there from seeds. It grew much more vigorously in the nonserpentine Stanford soil than on its native hill and was found to have 8 pairs of chromosomes very similar to those of *Layia.* Crossings were attempted between it and 8-chromosome Layias and Madias. The *Madia* crossings were unsuccessful, but the new plant crossed with two *Layia* species. The hybrid with *Layia glandulosa*

proved to be fertile, and the 8 plus 8 chromosomes from two supposedly distinct genera and tribes paired perfectly, indicating a very
close evolutionary relationship.

Figure 32 shows potted plants of *Layia glandulosa,* the new plant,
and the hybrid. *Layia glandulosa* Hook. et Arn., known as the desert
Layia, is a spring-flowering, white-rayed tarweed from sandy habitats,
occurring from Lower to central California on the coast side of the
mountains and from Arizona to Washington in the desert regions
of the Great Basin. The peculiar new form differs from it not only

Fig. 32. The discovery of the relationship of a rare relict through a crossing experiment. *Left, Layia glandulosa. Right,* the relict, originally thought to belong to a
different tribe. *Center,* their F_1 hybrid.

by the lack of rays but also by the pappus, which is short, stubby, and
brown in the new form as compared with the long, glistening, white
pappus in *glandulosa.* The hybrid of these two was a tarweed in
good taxonomic standing, for it had 3 to 8 rays per head, with accompanying bracts that in turn enclosed the seeds. However, some of
the heads on the same plant had no rays at all later in the season.

Figure 33 shows flower heads of the parents, of the F_1 hybrids,
and of some sample F_2's. The F_1 was completely fertile, and a large
and very vigorous second generation resulted. Forms with 8, 5, 3,
1, and no rays were segregated, some having long, others medium, and
still others very short rays. The seed-enfolding bracts always accom-

panied the rays. The color and length of the disk pappus varied from one parental extreme to another. It turned out that although the new form had no rays, it nevertheless carried a gene for light-yellow ray color.

The segregated F_2 types resolved the parental differences in so many steps that a completely graded series of variants was obtained. Two pairs of genes determine whether or not the plant has rays, other genes the number of rays; three are responsible for the length of the pappus, and several for its color. It was estimated that probably a maximum of 20 pairs of genes are responsible for the very striking differences that characterize these two forms, and several of these genes show genetic linkage.

It was concluded that the new form is a subspecies of *Layia glandulosa,* probably an edaphic race adapted to the serpentine soil, and possibly an ancient relict. It is significant that the differences between these two subspecies are comparable with differences that may characterize genera or even larger groups of plants. Such characters can be inherited like ordinary Mendelian differences, the main distinction being that in the groups of higher order such key differences are incorporated in independent genetic systems that cannot be broken up without seriously affecting the vitality of the offspring, whereas in the present case they are not so incorporated, but are included within the limits of a single species.

An early stage in interspecific differentiation— The evolutionist is on the lookout for biological entities that are in the transitional stage between the subspecies and true species. Such an example can be found in the coast tarweed of California, *Hemizonia angustifolia,* a 10-chromosome annual species of the *Madiinae* (Clausen, Keck, and Hiesey, 1947). It occupies a narrow strip on the coastal side of the outer Coast Range, extending inland only as far as the coastal fog belt. It is composed of two major races: one occupies a strip 275 miles long from northern California to south of Monterey Bay; the other starts 40 miles farther south and extends over a distance of 40 miles. It is separated from the northern subspecies by the Santa Lucia Mountains, which rise precipitously from the ocean, leaving no

Fig. 33. The inheritance of presence of ray florets in a cross between *Layia glandulosa* and the relict form without ray florets. *Top, left,* flower heads of two individuals of typical *glandulosa* (P$_1$), one with narrow, the other with wide rays. *Top, right,* two heads of the rayless relict form (P$_2$). *Second row,* variation in the F$_1$ in number of ray florets; the heads that first develop have the largest number of rays, and the latest may have none. *Three lower rows,* segregation in the F$_2$. (From Clausen, Keck, and Hiesey, 1947.)

coastal foreland for this species to occupy. Geographically the two subspecies are therefore effectively separated, but ecologically their habitats are of the same kind.

The morphological differences that separate the northern and the southern races are small but significant, and the two have even been recognized as species. Some of the differences can be seen in figure 34. The northern form has a low and broad habit, slender and open branching, and relatively small heads. The southern form has more erect and robust branching and larger and more densely congested heads. These differences are small as species differences go, but each of them depends upon the action of series of multiple genes, each with a small additive effect. In this matter, the slight morphological differences are resolved into even smaller steps, giving the impression of continuous variation.

The hybrid between the northern and the southern forms is completely fertile, and in an F_2 population of 1152 individuals, plants were recovered that in single characters were like one or the other of the parents, but never any that matched either parent in all of its characters. Such a situation suggests that the differences between the parents were determined by a moderate number of genes.

There were, however, other differences of less tangible nature. Although the F_1 was vigorous and 57 per cent of the offspring were as vigorous as either parent, the remainder were substandard in vigor and developed more slowly. The weak plants ranged from types that were only moderately weaker than the parents, namely, from 35 cm. across, to plants that were only 5 cm., forming a perfectly graded series.

These slower-growing plants seemed to be as healthy as the more vigorous ones; they continued to flower, although there was little or no increment in growth. Whereas these plants made little or no progress during the seven to eight months that they lived, the vigorous fraction grew until they were about a thousand times as voluminous as the most extreme dwarfs.

The genes that govern the physiological processes affecting the rates of growth in the two subspecies are therefore apparently not identical. These subspecies have developed fairly independently

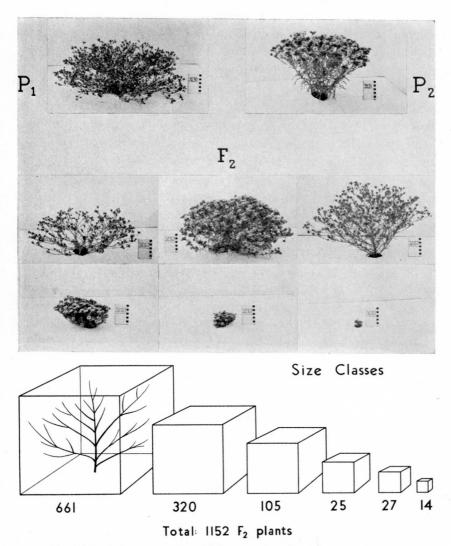

Size Classes

661   320   105   25   27   14

Total: 1152 F₂ plants

Fig. 34. Divergence in the genetic systems of two geographical races of *Hemizonia angustifolia*. *Top, left,* the northern race (P_1); *right,* the southern race (P_2). F_2, three vigorous and three substandard segregants; the scale beside each plant is 10 cm. high. The F_2 size classes are represented by cubes, the edges of which are 50, 35, 25, 15, 10, and 5 cm., respectively, and the numerals below indicate the number of plants in each class. The cube to the left represents the class with growth comparable to that of the parental forms. (From Clausen, Keck, and Hiesey, 1947.)

within periods of a geologic order of magnitude, and their gene systems have become different enough so that they no longer are completely interchangeable without detrimental effects to the progeny. Within each of the two subspecies a balanced metabolism is ensured by the interaction of their systems of genes, but when the subspecies are crossed, their gene systems are reshuffled as the second-generation hybrids develop. This process results in some combinations where the actions of the genes are not properly synchronized, and the metabolic balances have been upset. In contrast, the hybrid vigor in the interracial hybrids of *Layia* is maintained through the second and in some cases the third generation.

Evolutionarily the two entities of *Hemizonia angustifolia* are in the transitional stage between subspecies and full-fledged species. Many small steps were required to produce these differences, and many genes were altered, but the changes did not affect the direct interfertility of the subspecies or the structure of their chromosomes. Biological entities in such transitional stages of development are significant because their existence indicates gradual steps in the evolution of species.

Ecological races and morphological subspecies are therefore evolutionary entities that are distinguished by a considerable number of genes of the multiple type. These races often have developed systems of genes having opposing effects, and these provide a mechanism for expressing great variability. The genes that determine both the morphological differences and the fitness to the environment are often organized into genetic systems and are linked together. Each race, and each subspecies, therefore, serves as a package of potential variability that can be released when the environments change, causing the entities to migrate into new habitats where they may come near to other races. Such a juxtaposition of forms that previously were separated may result in rapid, or "explosive," evolution. Ecological races or morphological subspecies of one species are much more flexible than are distinct species, and at this stage new entities may therefore evolve fairly rapidly.

The Evolution of

Interspecific Barriers

THE process of separating groups of ecological races and geographical subspecies into distinct species is usually a very gradual one, and
it can be accomplished in many different ways. Essentially, what
happens is that two segments of what was formerly one species become separated by barriers to free interbreeding of one kind or another. In *Hemizonia angustifolia,* discussed in Chapter V, the
northern and the southern subspecies are in the process of evolving
genetic barriers in addition to geographic ones. This species provides
a good example of the dynamics of the process, because the genetic
barriers here are in an early stage of evolution.

The interspecific barrier to interbreeding must be viewed against
the background of the situation within species where such barriers
have not as yet started to evolve. *Layia platyglossa* is such an example. Figure 35 is a diagram of crossings performed within that
species, using 14 different populations native to geographically and
ecologically contrasting habitats within the range of the species.
Crosses have been made between populations that differ most widely
in relation to morphology, ecology, and geographical distribution.
Except for the hybrids of one strain, which itself has shown poor
fertility even in intrapopulation pollinations, all the other hybrids
were at least as vigorous and as fertile as the parents, and some of
their second generations were even more vigorous, on the whole,
despite the fact that some of the parents belonged to very contrasting

forms. This is in sharp contrast to the situation in *Hemizonia angustifolia,* where the second generation was weaker than the parental subspecies.

A barrier to interbreeding may evolve at some point in the natural range of distribution of a series of ecological races or local popula-

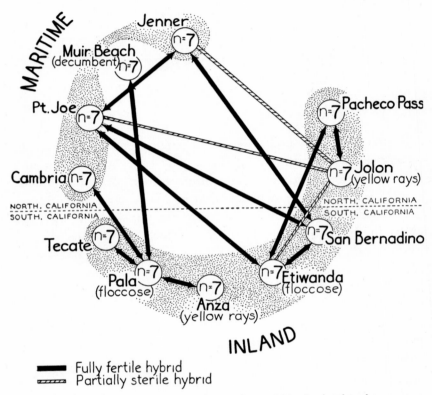

MARITIME

Jenner
n=7

Muir Beach
(decumbent) n=7

Pt. Joe
n=7

Pacheco Pass
n=7

Cambria n=7

Jolon
n=7 (yellow rays)

NORTH. CALIFORNIA
SOUTH. CALIFORNIA

NORTH. CALIFORNIA
SOUTH. CALIFORNIA

Tecate
n=7

n=7 San Bernadino

Pala
(floccose)
n=7

n=7
Anza
(yellow rays)

n=7 Etiwanda
(floccose)

INLAND

━━━ Fully fertile hybrid
▱▱▱ Partially sterile hybrid

Fig. 35. Diagram of intraspecific crossings within *Layia platyglossa.*

tions of a species. Such a barrier will gradually cause the resulting segments of the species to continue their evolutionary processes more independently of each other than before. Barriers of this kind exist in some species between certain of its populations, but as long as such populations are interfertile with others, the latter may serve to transfer genes between the intersterile populations. Such an arrangement is found within *Layia glandulosa,* a subspecies of which was discussed in Chapter V. A diagram indicating the results of crossings between eight of its populations belonging to three subspecies is shown in figure 36. The populations are arranged more or less as they occur in the wild in the order north to south and west to east.

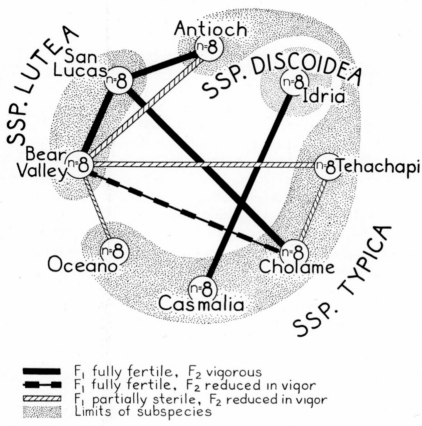

F₁ fully fertile, F₂ vigorous
F₁ fully fertile, F₂ reduced in vigor
F₁ partially sterile, F₂ reduced in vigor
Limits of subspecies

Fig. 36. Diagram of intraspecific crossings within *Layia glandulosa.*

Five of the crossings indicate the presence of partial genetic barriers, whereas the other four are completely interfertile. The genetic barriers within *glandulosa* are not correlated with either morphological or ecological differences, for the parents of some of the fully fertile hybrids with vigorous F₂ offspring belong to different subspecies, whereas in one case there is partial sterility between populations belonging to one subspecies and from the same ecological zone. If but few intermediaries remain between two sectors of a species, and these in the course of geologic history are wiped out, then the remnants may become completely separated species.

We find species in all stages of differentiation. The most distinct ones, those that are the end products of the processes of speciation, differ in morphological characters, in ecological fitness to the environment, in the genetic systems by which they control this fitness, and in the homology of the chromosomes. The differentiating processes, however, do not always proceed simultaneously at the same rate along all the fronts mentioned. In ecological races of one species, physiological differentiation precedes the morphological and the genetic. In other cases morphological differentiation will be far ahead, and in still others, genetic separation begins even before physiological differences have enabled the forms to occupy different environments, or before morphological differences have provided satisfactory taxonomic labels for distinguishing the species. The most normal pattern of speciation, however, is a more or less simultaneous and gradual separation in morphologic, ecologic, genetic, and cytologic characteristics.

There are numerous ways in which groups of populations and races may become genetically isolated from one another. We shall consider some of the mechanisms and stages of the evolution of interspecific barriers.

Groups having predominantly ecological barriers— In ecological races of one species, physiological differentiation precedes the development of morphological and genetical discontinuities. Some of the races of *Achillea* and *Potentilla glandulosa* from the central California transect which were discussed in Chapter V exemplify this kind of development. Races of this kind have not received taxonomic recognition because there are no morphological characters that can be used to differentiate them. Nevertheless, some such races in *Achillea,* for example, are so distinct physiologically that, from an evolutionary standpoint, they have become significantly more differentiated than have entities having attained contrasting morphology only.

Groups having predominantly morphological differentiation—
Very remarkable morphological differences can arise within a species
without the introduction of barriers to free interbreeding. In Chapter V an example was presented showing a race of *Layia glandulosa*
from an isolated serpentine-soil hillside in the inner Coast Range of
California that has become so distinct morphologically that it was
thought to belong to a different tribe of the family. The existence of
such a race suggests how differences that normally distinguish tribes
of a family can arise within a species through a series of small sys-
tematic changes which accumulate to produce startling morphological effects but which have not affected the freedom with which genes
are interchanged. The possibility exists that this serpentine form is
a relict that was isolated when the other Layias started to evolve.

Another example of strong morphological differences that have
not been accompanied by the evolution of genetic barriers to interbreeding is found in the genus *Penstemon* of the figwort family,
the *Scrophulariaceae*. *Penstemon Newberryi* Gray and *Davidsonii*
Greene meet in the high Sierra Nevada at altitudes of 10,000 to 10,-
500 feet, where they hybridize. They and part of the alpine population are shown in figure 37 (Clausen, Keck, and Hiesey, 1940).
Newberryi is a low shrub which extends from mid-altitude to Timberline. It has bright red trumpet-shaped flowers. *P. Davidsonii,* on
the other hand, is a strictly high-altitude cushion plant with blue,
big-throated flowers. The two species hybridize wherever they meet,
the hybrids are fully fertile, and hybrid swarms arise. The chromosome number is the same in both, and the chromosomes pair perfectly in the hybrids, as shown in figure 37. Despite such genetic
compatibility and the presence of the hybrid swarms in localized
areas of contact, the two parent species keep distinct, and their genes
do not appear to migrate far from the point of contact.

Evidently there are selective forces constantly in operation that
keep these species distinct. One of these forces is the environment,
which is operative between all ecological races, but it would hardly
cause such striking differences in flowers. More likely, these latter
differences are related to the system of pollination. It has long been
known that the narrow-throated red Penstemons are pollinated by

hummingbirds, and the blue, wide-throated flowers of *Davidsonii* have the right shape and color to attract bumblebees. Both humming-birds and bumblebees are active at these high altitudes. Continuous selection by pollinating agents in two different directions might

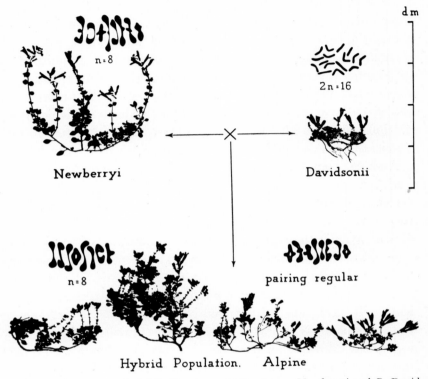

Newberryi

Davidsonii

Hybrid Population. Alpine

Fig. 37. Spontaneous hybridization between *Penstemon Newberryi* and *P. Davidsonii. Top, left, P. Newberryi* from 10,000 feet altitude with 8 pairs of chromosomes; *right, P. Davidsonii* from 11,500 feet, with 16 somatic chromosomes. *Below,* samples of a variable hybrid population at 11,000 feet with perfect pairing of the chromosomes. (Adapted from Clausen, Keck, and Hiesey, 1940.)

bring about morphological differences comparable to those commonly found between full-fledged species.

The wild columbines, the genus *Aquilegia* of the buttercup family, constitute another example. The species of this genus are as different as the little, nodding, red Canada columbine, *Aquilegia canadensis* L., and the very showy, blue and white, long-spurred

Colorado state flower, *A. caerulea* James, which are placed in different sections of the genus but which nevertheless have no genetic barriers to interbreeding. All Aquilegias have the same number of chromosomes, namely, 7 pairs. Two representatives of these sections of the genus are found in California. *A. formosa* Fisch., very similar to *canadensis,* ranges from the lowlands at the coast to 10,000 feet altitude in the Sierra Nevada. Here it meets *A. pubescens* Cov., which is a high-altitude species ranging to 12,000 feet. *A. formosa* has red, nodding flowers with short spurs, and *pubescens* has large and showy, cream-white flowers with long spurs. Hybrid swarms exist in several places in the high Sierra Nevada where the two species meet (Clausen, Keck, and Hiesey, 1945); the hybrids are fully fertile, and their progeny segregate many recombinations, but the genes of the parent species do not appear to migrate far away from the points of contact.

In the summer of 1950 Dr. Verne Grant had an opportunity to observe the pollination in the columbines at Timberline, and found that hummingbirds pollinate both the red *formosa* and red hybrid segregates, but do not frequent plants of *pubescens* or any segregates with white flowers (Grant, 1951). The hawk moths, on the other hand, which operate during the night, visit *pubescens* and white hybrid segregates, but do not visit plants with red flowers, which are almost invisible at night. Bumblebees visit both species and are evidently the hybridizing agents. From then on, hummingbirds will select for red among the offspring, and hawk moths for white, leaving it to the bumblebees to stock the populations with new hybrids.

These are examples of pollinating systems in wild plants that may keep natural entities distinct morphologically even though there are no genetic barriers. Such internal genetic barriers are not needed to keep the inheritances apart when selection by external pollinating agents is constantly at work. A most conspicuous example of striking morphological differences that are maintained through selective insect pollination is found in the species and so-called genera of the orchid family.

Maize together with its semiwild relative, the Mexican teosinte, is another example where spectacular morphological differences have arisen without hindering the free interchange of genes. Man has probably been the constantly selecting agent, and no internal barriers to free interchange resulted from this selective process.

Groups having predominantly genetic barriers— There is one genus of the tarweeds of California which differs strikingly from the pattern of speciation in *Layia* of the same subtribe of the *Compositae* in that it has very strong barriers of sterility even between neighboring populations of one species. These populations are so similar in external appearance that they cannot be distinguished. This genus is *Holocarpha.* Such a situation is just the opposite of that found in the columbines, where great morphological differences have arisen but where there are no internal barriers to the interchange of genes.

The genus *Holocarpha,* as now understood on the basis of combined experimental, field, and morphological studies, contains four species, two with 4 and two with 6 pairs of chromosomes. The formal nomenclatorial transfer of three of these species from the genus *Hemizonia* has not been made as yet, and we shall therefore use the names in an informal way.

Prior to the clarification provided through the experimental analysis of this group, the accepted classification for its largest segment of species was simply *Hemizonia virgata* Gray with one variety *Heermannii* (Greene) Jeps. (Jepson, 1923–1925). The *virgata* complex occupies dry hillsides in the foothills surrounding the Great Valley of California and the dry coastal ranges of southern California. These plants germinate in the winter and spring, but except for a few spring-flowering races most of them make their principal growth during the dry warm summer, long after the grass has withered in late April. The fall-flowering races and species begin to bloom in August and continue during September and October. Tackshaped glands cover the herbage with a glutinous, viscid exudate of a very pungent and penetrating odor. These plants are among the most common in the dry inner ranges, having populations that densely cover areas varying in size from a few to many square miles and consisting of from tens of thousands to many millions of individuals per population.

It was soon discovered that what was called *virgata* had 4, and the variety *Heermannii* 6 pairs of chromosomes, evidence which gave new taxonomic significance to the variety as being a species. Cultures of 50 populations from the wild were therefore assembled in the Stanford garden for further study and for counting of the chromosomes. It was found that 11 populations hitherto classified with *virgata* had 6, and not 4, pairs of chromosomes and that all 6-chromosome populations, including the ones formerly classified as *virgata,* had yellow anthers, whereas the 4-chromosome plants had black anthers, morphological differences not hitherto considered. The 11 yellow-anthered, 6-chromosome *"virgata"* populations also had obconical involucres and open, paniculate inflorescences, whereas the black-anthered, 4-chromosome populations of *virgata* had cylindrical involucres and racemose inflorescences with short-pediceled, almost sessile heads. The new 6-chromosome species, which also was morphologically distinct from 6-chromosome *Heermannii,* was named *obconica* (Keck, 1935).

A field survey showed that the three species of the *virgata* complex can easily be recognized by macroscopic, morphological characters. In the inner Coast Ranges of central California they alternate with each other in distribution and form a mosaic. One valley will be populated with *Heermannii,* for example, another with *virgata,* and a third with *obconica,* or vice versa, in various permutations. Sterile interspecific hybrids occur in the low passes between the valleys where the species meet.

The results of the survey of the chromosome numbers of the 51 populations of the *virgata* complex are indicated in table 5, which

Table 5. Somatic chromosome numbers in 51 populations of three species of the *virgata* complex of the genus *Holocarpha*.

Chromosome number	Number of populations			
	virgata	*obconica*	*Heermannii*	Total
$2n = 8$	19	1	—	20
$2n = 10$	1	—	1 (hybrid)	2
$2n = 12$	—	11	18	29
Total	20	12	19	51

lists the somatic numbers. It will be noticed that the apparent regularity in chromosome number within each species is broken by three exceptions, but these are explainable on the basis of chromosome repatterning as indicated by the observed differences in chromosome morphology between populations within each species. The somatic chromosomes from root tips of all the species of the *virgata* complex

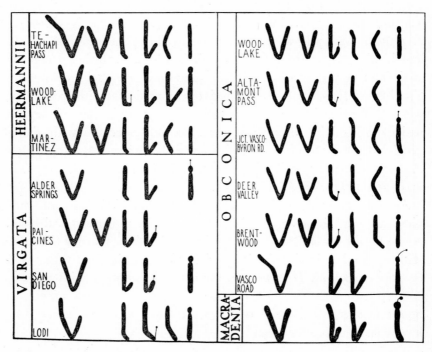

Fig. 38. Diagram of the somatic sets of chromosomes of 14 populations of 4 species of the genus *Holocarpha;* only one chromosome of each of the chromosome pairs is shown. See text.

are morphologically distinct, so that the individual chromosomes of each set can be recognized. Furthermore, the chromosome complements of different populations of the same species are also often noticeably distinct from each other. The distinctness, both in the morphology of the individual chromosomes and in the whole chromosome sets of the population, can be studied in figure 38, which shows diagrams of the somatic chromosome complements of samples of populations of the species of the *virgata* and *macradenia* complexes.

In *virgata,* as an example, the Alder Springs population from the northern part of California has one pair of V-shaped chromosomes, two J's, and one I-shaped satellited chromosome with subterminal constriction. Of the same species, the population from Paicines in central California has two V's, and the satellite has become attached to one of the two J's, but there is no I-shaped chromosome. The San Diego population in southernmost California has, again, one V and

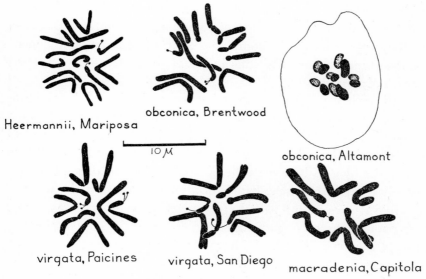

Heermannii, Mariposa

obconica, Brentwood

obconica, Altamont

virgata, Paicines   virgata, San Diego

macradenia, Capitola

10 μ

Fig. 39. Full chromosome complements of the four species of *Holocarpha*.

an I with subterminal constriction, but the satellite is on a J chromosome. Morphologically these three populations can hardly be distinguished, but cytologically they are extremely different.

It is obvious that extensive repatterning of the chromosomes must have taken place during the evolution of this group of species. The repatterning is evident not only between species but even in different local populations of the same species. An extreme case is the 4-paired *obconica* from Vasco Road shown in figure 38. One of the V-shaped chromosomes of this form is gone, but there is an extra arm on the other V; also, both arms of the two J's appear longer than in

97

other races of the species, and the satellited I chromosome is longer. The 5-paired *virgata* from Lodi, on the other hand, appears to have more chromosome material than do other races of that normally 4-paired species. There is the possibility, however, that the 5-paired forms are fairly recent hybrids between species with 4 and 6 pairs of chromosomes.

The somatic chromosomes of the root tips and the meiotic chromosomes of the pollen mother cells in the flower buds are large and of characteristic shapes. Figure 39 shows the somatic and meiotic chromosomes in the four species of the genus *Holocarpha*. These figures are drawn directly from chromosome plates of dividing cells as they appear under the compound microscope at an enlargement of 1800 times, linear. The scale indicates 10 microns, one one-hundredth of a millimeter.

With such striking interpopulation reorganization of the chromosome material in each species, it is not so remarkable that it is almost impossible to intercross even populations belonging to one species and that, in the rare cases where it has been possible to produce them, the hybrids between different populations of one species are usually completely sterile. Paradoxically enough, it is easier to cross 4-paired *virgata* with 6-paired *Heermannii* than it is to cross different populations of *virgata* together. The seed fertility of the *virgata* × *Heermannii* hybrids, however, is only a small fraction of 1 per cent, or none at all.

The assumption that the differences in the shape of the chromosomes have come about through interchange of segments of the chromosomes is confirmed by the behavior of the chromosomes in the hybrids, as can be seen from figure 40, which shows the chromosome pairing in the maturation divisions preceding the formation of pollen cells in a completely sterile F_1 hybrid, *virgata* × *Heermannii*. This is to be contrasted with the regular pairing in the parent species of chromosomes that are alike, shown in figure 39. In the hybrid there is little pairing between the 4 and 6 chromosomes that it received from its parent species, but whenever pairing occurs, then it is often between a long and a short chromosome, so that the pairs have the appearance of heterochromosomes, the paired unlike chromosomes that determine sex in monosexual organisms. Evidently, the long V chromosomes of one species are homologous with some of the shorter J or I chromosomes of the other. Also, the occurrence of chromatin bridges and lost fragments of chromosomes, phenomena which characterize hybrids having inversions of segments in their chromosomes, is prominent in maturation divisions, as illustrated by several pollen mother cells in figure 40.

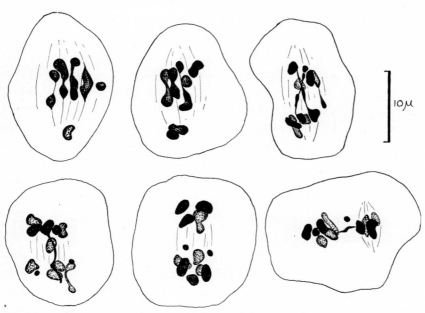

Fig. 40. Chromatin bridges, chromosome fragmentation, and pairing between unequally sized chromosomes in the F_1 of *Holocarpha virgata*, $n = 4$, $\times$ *H. Heermannii*, $n = 6$.

Extremely strong barriers to interbreeding have therefore been built up in this genus simply by interchanging pieces of chromosomes. In the wild, there is full interfertility within the local population, with its millions of individuals that often cover many square miles. Each such population is a breeding unit by itself and genetically sharply separated from its neighbors. As one moves from one valley in the inner Coast Range to the next, a different population or a different species will be present, and sterile natural hybrids occur at the point of contact. In gross morphology, however, one finds only very slight differences between populations of the same species—much less, in fact, than in *Layia* or in *Viola*. In *Holocarpha,* distinct populations belonging to one species evidently possess largely the same genes, although the genes have become rearranged within and between the chromosomes. The ecological features of the habitats of the three species of the *virgata* group in the dry interior of California are also essentially the same.

One of the keys to the understanding of the evolutionary situation in this group of tarweeds was to be found in a rare species on the verge of extinction which had been placed in a different genus, *Holocarpha macradenia* (DC.) Greene, at that time the only member of the genus. This rare species unfortunately occupied sites of future subdivisions of coastal towns in central California. It had previously been collected south of Oakland, where San Leandro is now located, at San Francisco, and at Ross in Marin County, but all of these localities have now become city residential areas. It was finally found again growing in an undeveloped subdivision east of Santa Cruz and on a golf link at Capitola, both localities overlooking Monterey Bay, and also in a grainfield east of Watsonville, a little farther removed from the coast. These plants had the tack-shaped, viscid glands, the pungent odor, and the same floral arrangement as have the three species of the *Hemizonia virgata* complex, but the gross appearance of the coastal species was very different: its heads were much larger and densely clustered, its habit was lower, and it had a short central stem and short, divergent branches. It was realized that such differences distinguish many strictly coastal races or species from their near relatives in the interior. At the time of the collection, speculations were made regarding its chromosomal compositions and its genetic relationships to the three species of the *virgata* complex in the interior foothills.

It was soon found that all three existing populations of the coastal *Holocarpha macradenia* had four pairs of chromosomes of the shape characteristic of species of the *virgata* complex (figs. 38 and 39) and that it had black anthers like *virgata*. Also, it crossed easily with all three species of the *virgata* complex; in fact, it crossed more easily than those species, or than different populations of *virgata* cross with each other. Moreover, the *virgata* $\times$ *macradenia* hybrid was 12 per cent seed-fertile, and the four *macradenia* chromosomes showed fair homology with the four from *virgata*. In the pollen mother cells of the F_1 hybrid the parental chromosomes formed various configurations of chains, pairs, and singles. In some cells there was a chain of six and a pair of two; in others a chain of four and two pairs; a chain of three, two pairs, and one single; or three pairs and two singles; the total always added up to the eight chromosomes that the hybrid received from its parents. Proof of the close genetic relationship of *macradenia* with *virgata* is therefore provided, both in the pairing between the chromosomes and in the moderate fertility of the hybrid. The two are, nevertheless, distinct species but hardly different genera.

The F_2 plants of the *virgata* $\times$ *macradenia* hybrid were derived from gametes that had passed through rigid selection during the gametic and embryonic stages, which permitted only 12 per cent of the seeds to be viable. Moreover, even of these, only 18 per cent germinated, providing us with only 156 F_2 plants from a large quantity of seed harvested on 11 F_1 plants isolated for mutual pollination by bees. The surviving F_2 plants, which had passed through these selective screens, were all healthy and vigorous, and also very variable, as can be seen from figure 41, which illustrates in the top row the two parental species, with the F_1 in the center showing hybrid vigor. In the two rows below are four of the F_2 plants. A summary of the segregation is presented in table 6, which indicates the extraordinary

Table 6. Segregation in F_2 of *Holocarpha virgata* $\times$ *macradenia* (F_1 12 per cent fertile).

Inflorescence	Width of involucre	Frequency
	mm.	
congested	8–10	17 (7 of *macradenia* type)
"	4–8	23
"	0–4	—
racemose	8–10	3
"	4–8	95 (3 of *virgata* type)
"	0–4	18 (15 of *virgata* type)
Total		156 (25 of parental types)

frequency of the parental types among the F_2's, amounting to 16 per cent of the total, 7 of the *macradenia* type, and 18 of the *virgata* type. One of the segregated *macradenia* plants is shown in the lower

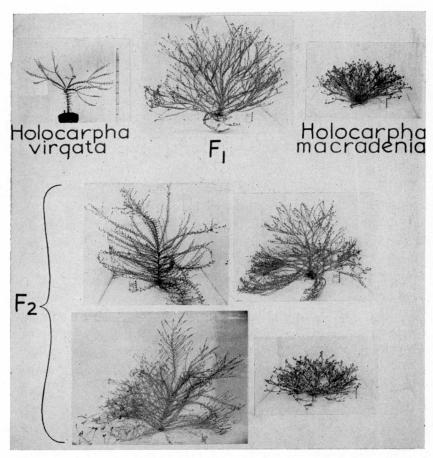

Fig. 41. Segregation in the cross between *Holocarpha virgata* and *H. macradenia*, species previously thought to belong to different genera. *Top row*, the parent species and the vigorous F_1. *Two lower rows*, four types of the F_2; *bottom, left*, racemose inflorescence as in *virgata*; *bottom, right*, an F_2 that is almost indistinguishable from the paternal grandparent, *macradenia*.

right corner of figure 41. The F_1 from which this plant was derived was harvested on *virgata*. The low number of chromosomes favor the frequent recurrence of the parental combinations in the F_2, especially if little crossing over between the chromosomes takes place. It is also apparent that selection in the gametic and embryonic stages greatly favors the survival of the parental combinations.

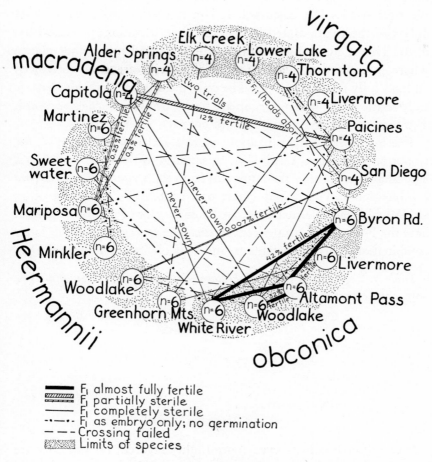

Fig. 42. Crossing polygon of 19 populations of the four species of the genus *Holocarpha*.

It was fortunate that *macradenia* was still available when these experiments were performed, for *Holocarpha macradenia* is probably by now an extinct species. Its two habitats at Santa Cruz and Capitola are now occupied by city dwellings and streets, and the area near Watsonville has become an intensely cultivated vineyard where no mere tarweeds are permitted.

Figure 42 summarizes in a crossing polygon the results of the 34 different crossings performed between 19 different populations of the four species just discussed. It is a most unusual situation that only 5 of the 13 attempted intraspecific hybridizations produced hybrids. This is in strong contrast with *Layia* and most other plants, where interpopulation and interracial hybrids are easily produced and are fully fertile (fig. 35). The only intraspecific hybrids that are fully fertile in the present group are four within the species *obconica*. Ten intraspecific hybridizations did not even produce an F_1.

The interspecific hybridizations were a little more successful, for 10 out of 21 attempts resulted in F_1's, and 5 of these produced F_2's. The most successful of the latter was from the *virgata* $\times$ *macradenia* combination just discussed (table 6). Another F_2 consisting of 15 individuals was obtained from an F_1 of *virgata* $\times$ *Heermannii,* but here the F_1 was only 0.3 per cent fertile. The segregation in this latter combination is listed in table 7, and it is obvious that here the pa-

Table 7. Segregation in F_2 of *Holocarpha virgata* $\times$ *Heermannii* (F_1 only 0.3 per cent fertile).

Classification	No. of individuals	Fertility, per cent
virgata type	7	14–21
Heermannii type	2	23–26
recombinations	2	0.45–0.50
triple hybrids, *virgata* $\times$ *Heermannii* $\times$ *macradenia*	4	16–35

Total: 11 F_2 + 4 triple hybrids.

rental combinations are even more highly favored, for not only are they the most frequent but they also have nearly fifty times as high a fertility as the two recombination types. The F_2 had to be obtained by open pollination in the field, because the F_1 was extremely sterile. Four triple hybrids were also obtained, and they were even more fertile than were the segregated parental types. These results indicate the extremely strict selection that operates in gametic and embryonic stages in hybrids that are so sterile.

The fact that all of the four species are interrconnected by hybrids suggests that *macradenia, virgata, Heermannii,* and *obconica* all belong in one genus, but the question then arises whether they should be members of the genus *Hemizonia* or should form a distinct genus of their own, that of *Holocarpha.* The facts overwhelmingly favor the latter conclusion. The four species have similar morphological characters and similar chromosomes, and are distinct from those of *Hemizonia.* Moreover, the four species are interconnected by hybrids, and none of them has ever crossed with any species of *Hemizonia,* although many different crossings were attempted and many others were invited through close planting in isolation plots.

The four species of *Holocarpha* form an evolutionarily closely knit group, a fact that is emphasized by their geographic distribution as indicated in figure 43. The few modern isolated populations of *macradenia* along the Pacific coast are now geographically well separated from the very extensive populations of the *virgata* complex in the dry interior, but the close genetic relationship of the group on the coast with the interior one suggests that the two probably were interconnected as maritime and inland races of one species before the Coast Ranges arose in the early Quarternary period. This event provided the dry interior habitats now so completely exploited by the three interior species, which are distributed there in a mosaic pattern.

Repatterning of the chromosomes is a mechanism that leads to a quick development of genetic barriers to interbreeding. This kind of barrier differs, however, from the kind of genetic barriers found between other species in the *Madiinae,* and also from that found in many other groups of plants. The barriers in *Holocarpha* are produced by large and abrupt differences in chromosome organization, whereas the barriers in the other species seem to have arisen through very gradual evolution by many small changes in the genetic-physiologic systems.

Local populations of a species like *Holocarpha virgata* are in cytogenetic characteristics distinct species, but it would be impractical to classify them as taxonomic species, for they have only acquired one of the attributes of full-fledged species. If, however, these local races were to acquire both morphological and ecological distinctness in

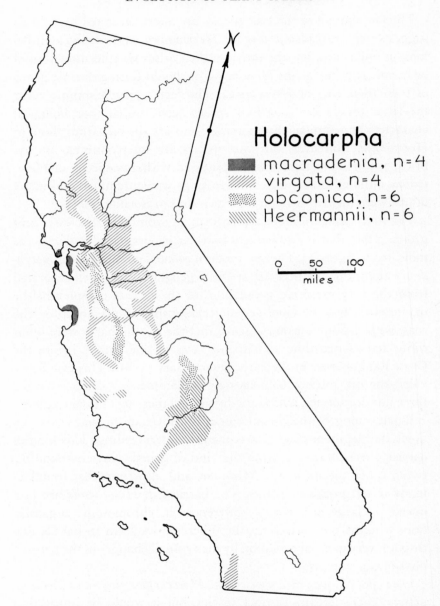

Fig. 43. The genus *Holocarpha*. The intermeshing distribution of the three species of the inner Coast Range and foothills, and the limited area once occupied by *H. macradenia* along the coast.

addition to their cytological differences, then they should certainly be recognized as taxonomic species.

Speciation through partial repatterning of the chromosomes is fairly widespread among both plants and animals. It appears to be the prevalent method of speciation in certain groups of species within *Oenothera* (Cleland, 1949), *Crepis* (Babcock, 1947), *Gilia* (Grant, unpubl.), some *Polemonium* (Clausen, 1931a), and many other genera. A classical example among insects is the species of *Drosophila* (Dobzhansky and others). Groups of species that have evolved by repatterning of chromosomes have the common characteristic of not being morphologically very distinct, but only rarely are the barriers to interbreeding in such organisms as sharp as in *Holocarpha*. There are two significant features of this type of cytogenetic separation. One is that a greater number of species of the same genus can exist in one area than by the more normal processes of differentiation through small changes in individual genes. The other feature is that speciation is much faster. Under certain circumstances such an arrangement might be an advantage to survival by quickly stabilizing a new form, and under others a disadvantage by reducing its flexibility.

Gradual stages in genetic and morphological differentiation— In the more typical species, the pattern of development of species from ecological races is through small steps involving the genetic and chromosome systems and the morphological characters. This process probably occurs over very long periods of time. Such a slow evolution of independent genetic systems is also likely to affect the morphological characters in small steps. The slow differentiation of genetic systems into intersterile groups is probably one of the most permanent ways in which species can evolve. Species that evolve in this way, and also those that evolve through repatterning of the chromosomes, bring their barriers along with them wherever they migrate, because they are separated from other species by internal barriers that are an integral part of their gene systems. The isolation brought about by selective pollinating agents, on the other hand, depends on constant selection to maintain the differences.

The differences between the northern and the southern subspecies of *Hemizonia angustifolia,* which were described in Chapter V, indicate how such barriers may begin. It was mentioned that in the hybrids the growth processes seemed to be upset, causing subnormal and dwarf offspring to appear.

An example of a somewhat stronger genetic barrier was found in the cross between two species of the so-called California fuchsias of the evening primrose family, *Zauschneria cana* Greene and *Z. septentrionalis* Keck (Clausen, Keck, and Hiesey, 1940). These species have red, trumpet-shaped flowers and are pollinated by hummingbirds. On the top line of figure 44 the parents of this cross are shown. To the left is *Z. cana,* which is a small semishrub that grows along the coast of southern California, and, to the right, *Z. septentrionalis,* an herbaceous cushion plant endemic to the redwood region of northern California. Both have 15 pairs of chromosomes, and at the present time they are geographically separated from each other by a distance of approximately 300 miles. The two species are easy to cross, and the F_1, shown below the parents, is vigorous, surpassing the parents. The hybrid was fertile and produced more than 2100 second-generation offspring by selfing, but many of the F_2's became slower in their growth about a month after they germinated. More than half of the offspring died early, and an additional 600 were very weak, like those illustrated at the bottom of figure 44. Only about 250 of the original 2100 had some promise of vigor, as exemplified by the center plant on the bottom line. Eventually all the F_2's displayed weakness in being attacked by mildew and rust, and after three years every F_2 plant had declined and become weak. The weakness of the F_2 plants affected their fertility, so that only the most vigorous produced seeds, and only small amounts, while others were sterile. The pairing of the chromosomes was regular in the vigorous F_1 hybrid. Here is obviously a case where the unrecombined parental genomes fit well together, but after the parental genes have been reshuffled in the F_1, the growth processes are upset and thrown out of balance so seriously that the final result is an elimination of about 100 per cent, even in the experiment garden, where there is no competition.

A similar example is found in *Layia gaillardioides* DC. (Hook. et Arn.) and *hieracioides* (DC.) Hook. et Arn. Both are natives of the central Coast Ranges of California, where there is some overlapping in their distribution. *Layia gaillardioides* has large, showy flower-heads, as seen in figure 45, and is self-sterile, whereas *hieracioides* has

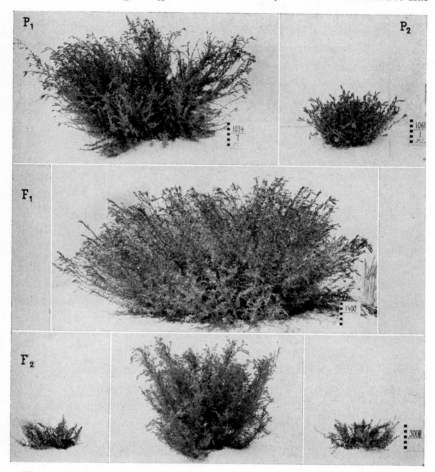

Fig. 44. Weak genetic barriers between two closely related species of *Zauschneria*, both with 15 pairs of chromosomes. P_1, *Z. cana;* P_2, *Z. septentrionalis.* F_1, the vigorous, shrubby, highly fertile first-generation hybrid. F_2, three samples of the weak second generation, including the most vigorous plant. All plants shown as grown in the Carnegie Institution garden at Stanford. (From Clausen, Keck, and Hiesey, 1940.)

small, inconspicuous flowers and is self-fertile. Both species have 8 pairs of chromosomes, and they cross easily to produce a fully fertile hybrid, showing normal pairing of chromosomes. The first-generation hybrid was fairly self-fertile, one individual producing 1850 F_2 individuals by selfing. It was evident, however, that already in early seedling stages a great number of slowly growing dwarfs were present, as indicated by figure 46. Each leaf shown is from a different plant, and there are many that are far below the standard of the parental species (P_1 and P_2) or the F_1. The unfitness of the second generation became more evident as the plants developed in the garden. Most of the dwarfs died early, but many of the vigorous plants developed much more slowly than did other Layias. Others had very few blooms or were

Fig. 45. Flower heads of two species of *Layia* and their hybrid. *Left, L. gaillardioides* self-sterile; *right, L. hieracioides,* self-fertile; *center,* the F_1, 50 per cent self-fertile.

otherwise substandard, and only 20 per cent of the germinated plants were as vigorous and floriferous as the parental species. In *Layia,* lack of resistance against the drought of the California summer is compensated for by speedy development which enables the species to bloom early during the moist spring. The interchange of genes in the hybrid of *gaillardioides* with *hieracioides* resulted in the development of lateness, a new character for *Layia* but an undesirable one for survival in the California climate, because lateness was not accompanied by development of protection against drought, as it is in other genera of the *Madiinae.* Genes that determine the morphological and physiological characteristics of wild species are built into complicated systems that are of necessity so balanced as to ensure fitness of the species to the complete seasonal cycle of the environment. These genetic systems differ even in species as closely related as *gaillardioides* and *hieracioides,* and when distinct species are intercrossed and their inheritances interchanged we may destroy these intricate balances.

The partial genetic barrier between *Layia gaillardioides* and *hieracioides* is reinforced also by their having different systems for pollination. Self-fertility and inconspicuous rays both tend to be dominant,

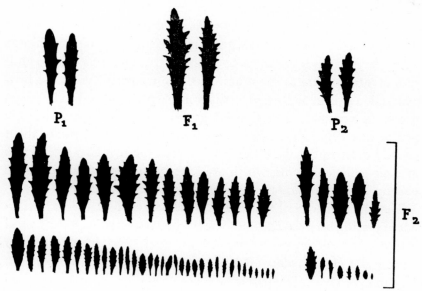

Fig. 46. Weak genetic barriers between two closely related 8-chromosome species of *Layia* as illustrated by basal leaves of the same age, one from each plant. *Top, left* (P_1), *L. gaillardioides; right* (P_2), *L. hieracioides; center* (F_1), the highly fertile first-generation hybrid. *Two lower rows* (F_2), samples of leaves of the second-generation offspring: *top row,* of normal vigor; *bottom row,* samples of slow-growing dwarfs.

and each of these two characters is determined by a series of multiple genes. There was no obvious genetic linkage between these two characteristics.

Both in the Layias and in *Zauschneria* the interspecific sterility was expressed not in seed sterility but in the weakness of the second generation. The sterility in most interspecific hybrids is expressed both in the abortion of seeds in the first generation and in weakness of the offspring in the second. Our next example is typical of the latter situation. It is a hybrid between a form of *Layia gaillardioides* DC., the coastal Layia, which is from the outer Coast Range, and *Layia penta-chaeta* Gray, the valley Layia from the San Joaquin Valley, both species having 8 pairs of chromosomes. Figure 47 shows photographs of pressed specimens of the parents, the F_1, and samples of the F_2. The pairing between the chromosomes was only slightly reduced in the hybrid, but the seed fertility was down to 1.6 per cent. A second generation of only 72 plants was produced from 10 large F_1 plants, and these were mainly weak and unhealthy. As a contrast to this interspecific hybrid we may consider a related intraspecific one, using the same valley race of *Layia pentachaeta* as one parent and a Sierran foothill race of *pentachaeta* as the other. In this intraspecific cross the first-generation hybrid had a seed fertility of 70.9 per cent, and 10 F_1 plants produced a second generation of 1254 vigorous, healthy, and fertile plants. In morphological characters the three parent forms are about equally distinct, but the difference between the first two extend also to their genetic systems, which are already so distinct that even the pairing of the chromosomes is beginning to be affected.

That the higher sterility in the F_1 is not necessarily caused by the reduced pairing between chromosomes is shown by figure 48 of a hybrid between two species of the hayfield tarweeds, *Hemizonia lutescens* Greene and *H. calyculata* (Babcock and Hall, 1924, as a subspecies of *H. congesta* DC.). The parents are not shown in this case; they are approximately of the size as the two top F_2 plants illustrated, and the first-generation hybrid is even more vigorous. Both parents have 14 pairs of chromosomes and the pairing between the chromosomes in the F_1 is normal, but the hybrid nevertheless was only 1.6 per cent seed fertile. Twelve large F_1 plants which were open-pollinated in the garden produced a second generation of only 159 plants from approximately 10,000 seeds, which were mainly aborted. Of the F_2 plants, only 68 were of a size similar to the parents; the remainder were subnormal or dwarfish in different degrees, 39 being so weak that they died prematurely.

In this as in the preceding examples of weak F_2 offspring, the weak plants were not of a specific genetic type that was being segregated, for there was a complete gradation ranging from vigorous plants to

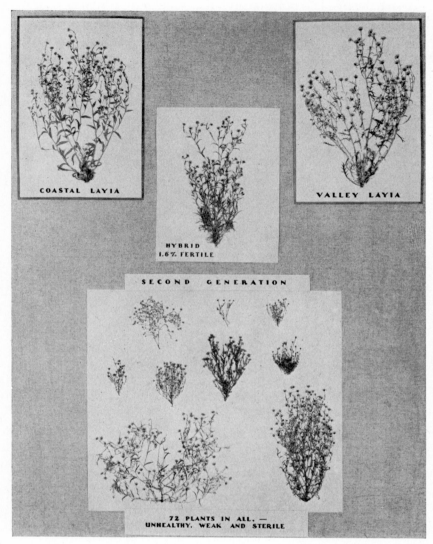

Fig. 47. Moderate genetic barriers between two 8-chromosome species of *Layia* belonging to one species complex. *Top row, left,* coastal *Layia*, the *L. gaillardioides* parent; *right,* valley *Layia*, the *L. pentachaeta* parent; *center,* the slightly fertile F_1. *Bottom,* samples of the weak F_2 offspring, including the two most vigorous plants. In contrast, an intraspecific hybrid between two subspecies of *pentachaeta* yielded 18 times as many F_2 plants, all vigorous and healthy.

extreme dwarfs. It is quite obvious that something is wrong with the metabolic processes of the progeny after the genes of the parental species have been recombined. The dwarfs and the vigorous plants were all set in the garden at the same time five months before the pictures were taken. They had been growing all the time, even the most ex-

F_2 of Hemizonia lutescens × calyculata

From 10,000 seeds, 159 F_2 plants $\begin{cases} 68 \text{ normal} \\ 52 \text{ subnormal} \\ 39 \text{ died prematurely} \end{cases}$

Fig. 48. Fairly strong genetic barriers between *Hemizonia lutescens* and *calyculata*. The F_1 had homologous chromosomes, but only 1.6 per cent of its seeds were able to germinate. *Top row,* two F_2 plants of a vigor comparable to that of the parents; *bottom row,* sample of subnormal and dwarf plants in the F_2, even the smallest mature and flowering. Height of scale is 10 cm. All plants grown in the Carnegie Institution garden at Stanford.

treme dwarfs, but there was very little increment in the latter. The smallest dwarf of the population is shown in the picture; it is only about 8 cm. tall and in first bloom five months after it was set in the garden. The uncrossed parental species, on the other hand, produced uniform and vigorous offspring.

An even more extreme case of sterility combined with normal pairing of the chromosomes was observed in the first-generation hybrid between two *Madia* species, namely, *M. elegans Wheeleri* and *M. citriodora* Greene, which are shown in figure 49. *Wheeleri* is self-sterile and *citriodora* is an habitual self-pollinator. Both species have 8 pairs of chromosomes. The crossing was made in an isolation plot in the

Fig. 49. Two 8-chromosome species of *Madia* that are separated by very strong genetic barriers, although their chromosomes are homologous. *Left, M. citriodora,* a small-rayed, self-fertile species; *right, M. elegans Wheeleri,* a large-rayed, self-sterile species. Their F_1 hybrid was highly sterile, producing only one F_2 plant from three F_1's.

garden, with one individual of the self-sterile species in the center surrounded by a ring of seven individuals of the self-fertile one, but only 5 F_1 hybrids were obtained on the central individual, even under such favorable conditions, a result which in itself suggests that the genetic relationship between these two species is very remote. Three first-generation hybrid individuals were isolated for mutual pollination in the open, but only one second-generation plant was obtained from all the seed harvested, the estimated fertility accordingly being only about 0.05 per cent.

In the hybrid, there nevertheless was almost normal pairing between the chromosomes of the parent species, and the chromosomes were distributed to the daughter nuclei as $8 + 8$ in 88 per cent of the cells, whereas the distribution was $7 + 9$ in the other 12 per cent of the cells investigated. Most cells in the tetrads from which the sex cells for the second generation arise had therefore received the full complement of 8 chromosomes. Each chromosome, however, contained various proportions of genes from both *citriodora* and *Wheeleri* on account of the previous pairing and the subsequent free crossing over. Some cells of the young tetrads started soon to disintegrate, as if the genes they had received were unable to carry on normal development in the microscopic gametophyte, the sexual generation that produces the sex cells. The fact that only some of the four cells of the tetrads disintegrated suggests that it is the gene complement inside the cell that caused the disintegration. The gene complement is composed of varying proportions of genes from both species. By the time the mature pollen was formed, the sterility effect was found to be much greater, for only 2 per cent of the pollen in the hybrid was good, as compared with 95 per cent in the parental species, and only 0.05 per cent of the seed possibilities resulted in F_2 plants.

At a later stage in the differentiation of species, the chromosomes have become so different that they are completely unable to inter-pair. As an example of species that have arrived at complete non-homology and inability to exchange their genes, we will consider two species of the genus *Madia* of the *Madiinae*, namely *M. nutans* (Greene) Keck with 9 pairs of chromosomes and *Rammii* Greene with 8 pairs (Clausen, Keck, and Hiesey, 1945). They and their hybrid are seen in figure 50. These species are relatively rare, *nutans* being confined to volcanic-ash soil of the inner north Coast Ranges of California and *Rammii* to the foothills of the central Sierra Nevada, where it grows in clay soils.

The F$_1$ hybrid between these two species has 17 unpaired chromosomes. Occasionally there may be a loose connection between one or two chromosomes which cannot be classed as real pairing. Figure 51 shows at the topmost line the somatic unpaired and the gametic paired chromosomes of both parent species. In the next line are seen the 17 chromosomes in the root tips of the hybrid, the lack of pairing of the gametic chromosomes in the pollen mother cells of the hybrid, and the subsequent irregular distribution of the chromosomes to the

Fig. 50. Two *Madia* species that are separated by very strong genetic barriers and by lack of homology between their chromosomes, and their amphiploid hybrid. *Left*, *M. nutans* with 9 pairs of chromosomes; *right*, *M. Rammii*, with 8 pairs; *center*, their vigorous, fertile, amphiploid hybrid, *M. nutrammii*, with 17 pairs of chromosomes. (From Clausen, Keck, and Hiesey, 1945.)

daughter nuclei from which the sex cells arise. Occasionally this irregular distribution will lead to the formation of sex cells that contain all the chromosomes of both parents, and consequently also all their genes.

The individual chromosomes of such a hybrid, in which no pairing takes place, will always retain their identity because they have been unable to interchange genes by crossing over. This is in marked contrast with those interspecific hybrids that have homologous chro-

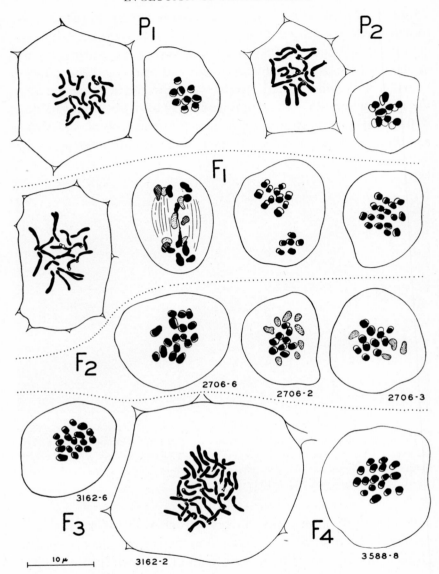

Fig. 51. The chromosome relationships of *Madia nutans*, *M. Rammii*, and their hybrid, resulting in the origin of the amphiploid species *M. nutrammii*. *Top*, P₁, 18 root-tip chromosomes and 9 pairs of gametic chromosomes in the first maturation division of the pollen mother cells of *M. nutans*; P₂, 16 root-tip chromosomes and 8 pairs of gametic chromosomes in *M. Rammii*. *Second row*, F₁, *left to right:* 17 root-tip chromosomes; first maturation division in side view with only one loose pair; second

mosomes, because genic interchange takes place in the latter in each new generation.

Only those sex cells of the *Madia nutans* $\times$ *Rammii* hybrid that contained either all the chromosomes of one of the parents or all the chromosomes of both were able to function. After several generations of natural selection in the garden, only plants that contained two sets of all 17 chromosomes from both of the parent species survived. When such plants produce sex cells, their chromosomes form 17 pairs, 9 of which came from *nutans* and 8 from *Rammii*. Hybrids of this kind faithfully distribute the unchanged complements from both of their parent species to all of their offspring in subsequent generations. The vigor and the uniformity of the *nutrammii* hybrid with the doubled number of chromosomes is in contrast to the disturbed and upset development of offspring of interspecific hybrids that have homologous chromosomes. Such hybrids can interchange the genes of their intricately balanced but specifically different genetic systems, and this interchange is detrimental to the progeny.

The *Madia nutans* $\times$ *Rammii* hybrid with the doubled number of chromosomes is morphologically similar to the first generation, and differs from both parent species, as shown in figure 50. In succeeding generations it is fertile and constant, and behaves as a new species that had added the entire inheritances of both the parent species. Such species are called amphiploids, meaning "both folded together."

This new species, which was named *Madia nutrammii* after its parents, arose twice in our experimental gardens independently and spontaneously. Many wild plant species appear to have arisen the same way. Such amphiploid species have characters that generally

---

maturation division with chromosomes unevenly distributed as 11 to one and 6 to the other daughter nucleus and each preparing to divide again; *right*, second maturation division with all 17 chromosomes from both parent species in one group preparing to divide. *Third row*, F_2, first maturation divisions in three plants; *left*, the stable amphiploid combination with 17 pairs of chromosomes; *center*, irregular plant with 9 pairs and 8 singles; *right*, another with 11 pairs and 4 singles. *Bottom row*, *left*, pollen mother cell with 17 pairs and root-tip cell with 34 chromosomes of an amphiploid F_3 plant; *right*, F_4 of an amphiploid with 17 pairs of chromosomes. (From Clausen, Keck, and Hiesey, 1945.)

are intermediate between those of their parent species, and they usually occupy a different niche in the environment. At this stage in evolution, the complete heredity of the species acts as a unit that can be added to that of another species, rather than as individual genes that can be exchanged. The development in different species of nonhomologous sets of chromosomes, therefore, represents an important stage in the evolution of plant species.

Fig. 52. Two 8-chromosome species of *Layia* that are genetically so remotely related that their genomes cannot even combine to produce a successful F_1. *Left, L. gaillardioides; right, L. heterotricha; center*, their most vigorous F_1 hybrid, 8 cm. tall, with one flower head.

We do not know the steps that are involved in chromosomes' becoming nonhomologous. Great genetic changes can take place without affecting the capacity of chromosomes to pair, and members of one species separated by extensive geographical barriers for millions of years may still preserve perfectly homologous chromosomes. Many intermediate stages in evolution from fully homologous to completely nonhomologous chromosomes are known. We do not even at the present time know why chromosomes pair in the first place. Until we know this, it is futile to theorize as to the reasons why chromosomes fail to pair in hybrids between remotely related species.

At an even later stage in evolutionary differentiation the species have become so distinct that their gene sets are incompatible and cannot even combine to form a viable hybrid. Such an example is seen in figure 52 in the F_1 of *Layia gaillardioides* (Hook. et Arn.) DC. crossed with *Layia heterotricha* (DC.) Hook. et Arn. Both of these species have 8 pairs of chromosomes; the former is a species of wooded regions in the Coast Ranges, the latter a relatively rare species of muddy, moist flats in the inner Coast Range. The individuals of these two species are self-incompatible so the crossing was performed in an outdoor isolation plot, with one individual of *gaillardioides* being surrounded by five *heterotricha*. Approximately 8000 seeds were harvested on the central *gaillardioides* plant and these were mainly empty. Only 13 F_1 plants germinated from this lot, and these seedlings were extremely dwarfish and weak, with poorly developed roots. Only 4 plants survived for two months, and only one of these, the most vigorous plant, reached the flowering stage, producing one tiny flower head. This plant, which was 8 cm. tall, is shown between the normally developed parent strains in figure 52. Its anthers were aborted, so no data on chromosome pairing could be obtained. From other crossings of *heterotricha* with species that are related to *gaillardioides,* it is known that their chromosomes are not homologous. This is an example of two species that are at a stage in evolutionary differentiation that approaches that of distinct genera.

There is a large borderland of present-day species in the making between such full-fledged species as have acquired ecological, genetical, chromosomal, and morphological distinctness and such races that only have ecological separation. The species exist in all stages of ecologic, genetic, cytologic, or morphologic distinctness, some preponderantly morphological, others preponderantly genetical, and still others preponderantly ecological. In more typical species, however, the three or four lines of differentiation appear to be progressing more or less simultaneously.

VII

The Evolution of

Groups of Species

AT a certain stage in the evolution of a group such as a genus, for example, its major subdivisions have become so distinct that hybrids between them are completely sterile. This separation has often been accompanied by complete differentiation of the chromosomes, so that the chromosomes of the parental species are no longer able to pair in the hybrid when species of such subgroups are crossed. When this stage has been reached, we say that full-fledged species complexes, or cenospecies, have evolved.

After the evolution of a genus has progressed this far, it is possible for several species in the genus to occupy the same habitat, because their genes cannot be interchanged. Such species will therefore remain distinct even if they occur together. Such an arrangement will enable a genus to place more species in a region than before. This stage in the evolution of the genus can be illustrated by the species of *Layia,* a genus of the sunflower family that has been referred to in the earlier chapters.

Groups of species in the genus Layia— The genus *Layia* is composed exclusively of spring-flowering California annuals that germinate during the winter and die before the dry season comes in June. Barring rare exceptions, they occur only at lower altitudes, occupying two or three of the major ecological zones in the Coast Ranges, the valleys, and the foothills of the Sierra Nevada.

Several species of *Layia* have been discussed in the preceding chapters. For the present discussion, two subspecies of the most showy species of the genus, *Layia pentachaeta* Gray, exemplify the genus in figure 53. The plant to the left is a very early blooming subspecies with white rays, occupying the west and south sides of the San Joaquin Valley, and the plant to the right is the typical yellow-rayed subspecies, which occupies slightly higher altitudes in the foothills

Fig. 53. Two races of *Layia pentachaeta*. *Left,* a white-rayed, early-blooming race from the west side of the San Joaquin Valley. *Right,* a yellow-rayed, later-blooming race from the foothills of the Sierra Nevada.

and lower ranges of the Sierra Nevada on the east side of this valley.

By developing several incompatible groups of species, the genus *Layia* has been able to crowd 14 species that retain their identity into the two or three ecological zones within its area. It is a combination of genetic and cytological relationships governing the development of intersterility groups, in addition to the development of geographical and ecological races, that has made this achievement possible. Finally, it is the morphological relationships that make it possible to recognize the entities. An analysis of these kinds of relationship will therefore aid us in understanding the evolutionary differentiation of the genus. Any one of these criteria of relationship which is applied to the exclusion of the others produces a one-sided conception of species relationship as compared with a conception based on all of them.

The chart in figure 54 represents a morphologic analysis of the relationships within *Layia* as determined by 15 characters, but it is also based on the results of crossings and the study of chromosomes and their behavior. For these reasons it is different from the pre-experimental concepts of relationship in the genus. A form, for example, that was called *Layia Calliglossa* Gray was found to be conspecific with *chrysanthemoides* (DC.) Gray (Chapter V, pp. 70–71). In contrast, another, *L. elegans* (Nutt.) Torr. et Gray (Chapter V, pp. 66–68) was found to consist of three forms that were split between the species *L. platyglossa* (Fisch. et Mey.) Gray, *L. glandulosa* Hook. et Arn., and a new species, *Layia septentrionalis*.[1] Moreover, experimental evidence indicated that the former *Layia nutans* (Greene) Jeps. belongs to the genus *Madia* rather than to *Layia*. The species lost were counterbalanced by some gains. It was found that the former *Layia hieracioides* (DC.) Hook. et Arn. contained two species, its southern component being *L. paniculata,* an undescribed new species with twice as many chromosomes as has *L. hieracioides*. Also, two very narrowly endemic species, *Layia Munzii* Keck and *leucopappa* Keck, were discovered, so that the net result of the experimental analysis is that the genus now is believed to have 14 species instead of the original 13.

These 14 species can be distinguished with the aid of about a dozen morphological characters, as indicated in figure 54. These characters involve all parts of the plant, especially the flowers. None of the species can be separated by single characters, but combinations of them can be used to key out the species. As to chromosome numbers, the species are divided into two major groups, those with 7 pairs and those with either 8 or 16 pairs. The chromosome situation in the

---

[1] Descriptions of this and other new taxonomic entities mentioned on succeeding pages are now in manuscript form and are to be published shortly by Dr. David D. Keck.

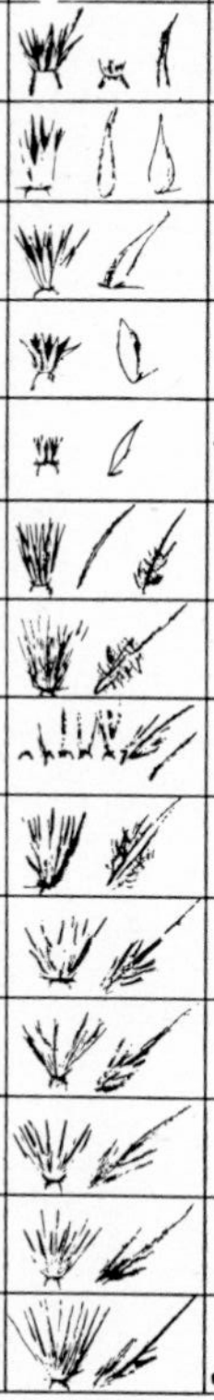

Fig. 54. Analysis of differences between the species of *Layia*.

Species	Chromosome Number	Inner Chaff	Involucre Glandular	Pappus (Paleaceous/Setose)	Pappus Detail	Pappus: Number of Units	Pappus (White/Rufous)	Anther-Color	Involucre (H/C/U)	Stems Dark-Dotted	Strongly Odorous	Self-Sterile	Ligule Conspicuous	Ligule Color	Disk-Corolla Length in mm	Soil
CHRYSANTHEMOIDES	n=7	+	–	P	(drawing)	CIRCA 10–16 (8)	W	B	H	–	–	+	+	Yellow with white tips	3–5	HEAVY
FREMONTII	n=7	+	–	P	(drawing)	9–12 (0)	W	B	H	–	–	+	+	Yellow with white tips	3.6–5.3	HEAVY
MUNZII	n=7	–	+	P	(drawing)	9–11	W	B	H	–	–	+	+	Yellow with white tips	3.6–5	ALKALI ADOBE
LEUCOPAPPA	n=7	–	+	P	(drawing)	10	W (bright white)	Y	H	–	–	+	+	White	3.7–5	HEAVY
JONESII	n=7	–	+	P	(drawing)	10–12(14) (0)	W	B	H	±	–	+	+	Yellow with white tips	3.1–5.2	LIGHT
PLATYGLOSSA	n=7	–	+	S	(drawing)	18–30 (0)	W	B (?)	H	(±)	–	+	+	Yellow with white tips; yellow (±)	4–6	VARIOUS
SEPTENTRIONALIS	n=8	–	+	S	(drawing)	16–21 (0)	W	Y	C	–	–	+	+	Yellow	5–8	SANDY
PENTACHAETA	n=8	–	+	S	(drawing)	10–18 (0–5)	W	Y	H	+	+	+	+	Yellow	3–5.5	LIGHT
GLANDULOSA	n=8	–	+	S	(drawing)	10 (–12)	W	Y	C	+	+	+	+	White; yellow (⊞)	4–6	SANDY
GAILLARDIOIDES	n=8	–	+	S	(drawing)	17–21 (0)	R	B	U	+	+	+	+	Yellow with white tips	3.5–5.2	LIGHT
HIERACIOIDES	n=8	–	+	S	(drawing)	11–15	R	B	C	–	+	–	(±)	Yellow	2.5–4	LIGHT
PANICULATA	n=16	–	+	S	(drawing)	12–13	R	B	C	–	+	–	–	Yellow	2.7–3.1	LIGHT
CARNOSA	n=8	–	+	S	(drawing)	25–33	R	B	C	–	–	–	–	White	2.5–3.5	COASTAL DUNES'
HETEROTRICHA	n=8	–	+	S	(drawing)	14–19 (deciduous)	W	Y	H	–	+	+	+	White (cream)	4.5–7	ADOBE

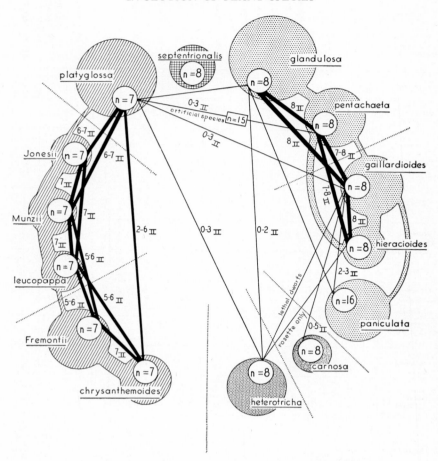

Fig. 55. Crossing polygon of *Layia*, showing cytogenetic relationships. The black lines connecting species indicate successful hybridizations, and the width of the lines, the approximate degree of pairing between the parental chromosomes in the hybrid. The widths of shaded connections between the species indicate degrees of gene interchange possible. Dotted radials indicate the major morphological discontinuities within the genus. See text. (From Clausen, Keck, and Hiesey, 1941.)

genus *Layia* and in other genera of the Madiinae was originally determined by D. A. Johansen (1933).

The diagrammatic crossing polygon, figure 55, summarizes the evidence obtained from crossing experiments, studies on chromosome behavior, and the analysis of morphological differences. The size of the connections between the species roughly indicates the degree with which genes can be "piped" from one species to another, and the thickness of the lines connecting species expresses the degree of homology between their chromosomes as determined by the percentage of pairing in the hybrid between such species. Heavy lines mean complete or nearly complete pairing, and thin lines no pairing, or almost none.

The major discontinuities, based solely on crossability, and the differences in chromosome number coincide quite well, but they are not always correlated with the morphological discontinuities, which are indicated by the dotted radial lines. The largest cytological barrier, for example, that between the 7- and 8-paired species, bisects also one of the major morphological groups, while on the other hand the large morphological gap between *Layia Jonesii* and *platyglossa* coincides with only one of the minor cytogenetic discontinuities.

It will also be seen that there are two major cytogenetic complexes of species in the genus, namely, one containing 6 and another containing 5 species. Within each of these complexes the species can, to a limited extent, exchange their genes, but no gene interchange is possible between different complexes. The individual species of such a complex are known as ecospecies, and, like ecological races, they often occupy ecologically different kinds of habitat.

The geographic areas of these 14 species form a distribution pattern that is closely related to their genetic kinships. The distribution patterns can be studied from figures 56 and 57.

In the 7-chromosome species complex (fig. 56), *Layia chrysanthemoides* (fig. 25, p. 69) and *Fremontii* form a species pair with *chrysanthemoides* in the northern Coast Ranges and with *Fremontii* in the foothills of the drier interior Sacramento and San Joaquin valleys. Farther south there are three rare species of very limited distribution, namely, *Jonesii* in sand near the coast, *Munzii* in muddy alkaline flats in the inner Coast Range (fig. 1, p. 13), and *leucopappa* on clay hillsides in the southern Sierra Nevada foothills. There is hardly any overlapping in the areas of these five species.

The 7-chromosome *Layia platyglossa* (fig. 22, p. 62) is almost a species complex by itself. It occupies the coastal strip north of the

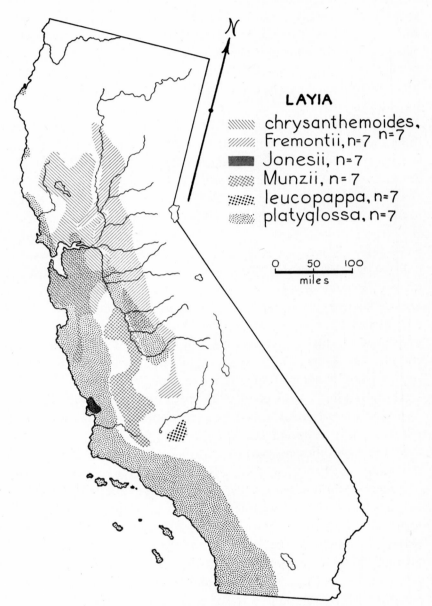

Fig. 56. Map of California, showing the distribution of the *Layia* species with 7 pairs of chromosomes.

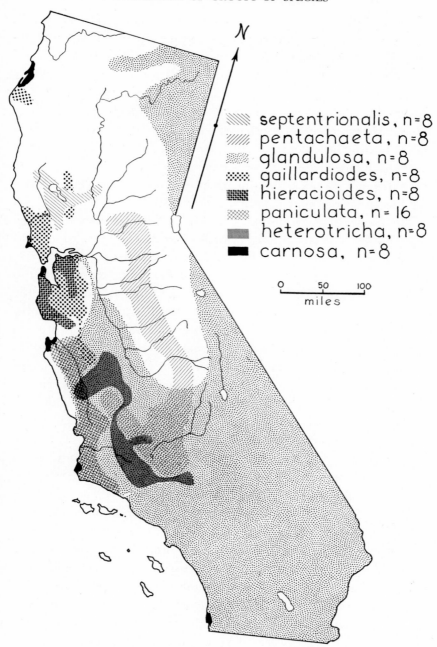

septentrionalis, n=8
pentachaeta, n=8
glandulosa, n=8
gaillardiodes, n=8
hieracioides, n=8
paniculata, n=16
heterotricha, n=8
carnosa, n=8

0   50   100
miles

Fig. 57. Map of California, showing the distribution of
the *Layia* species with 8 or 16 pairs of chromosomes.

San Francisco Bay, but south of the Bay its populations occur on hill-sides over most of the Coast Ranges and the valleys. It is genetically sharply separated from *chrysanthemoides* and *Fremontii* and can therefore be found growing together with them. It is more closely related genetically to the three rare species, *leucopappa, Munzii,* and *Jonesii,* but *leucopappa* is outside of the geographical range of *platy-glossa, Munzii* occupies a different edaphic niche, and *Jonesii* is very local, having little contact with *platyglossa.* Indirectly, *platyglossa* could exchange genes with *chrysanthemoides* and *Fremontii* through the three rare species as intermediaries, but there is very little chance for this to happen under natural conditions.

The species of the 8-chromosome genetic complex also occupy geographically and edaphically distinct habitats (fig. 57). *Layia gail-lardioides* and *hieracioides* (fig. 45, p. 110), and the tetraploid counterpart of the latter, *paniculata,* are Coast Range species occurring in that order from north to south in central California; there is little overlapping of their areas except on the San Francisco Peninsula between the first two. In the interior of central California there are two species of this complex which occur on different soils. These are *L. pentachaeta* (fig. 53, p. 123), on rocky, light clay hillsides surrounding the Great Valley, and *glandulosa* (fig. 32, p. 81), a species of deserts and sand that reaches the coast in sandy habitats southward and extends to Baja California, northward to eastern Washington and Idaho, and eastward to New Mexico.

Three of the 8-chromosome species of *Layia* each form a mono-typic species complex. These are *septentrionalis, heterotricha* (fig. 52, p. 120), and *carnosa* (Nutt.) Torr. et Gray. *L. septentrionalis* is unable to cross with any other species, but in morphological characters it is close to *pentachaeta* (fig. 54), and its area is distinct from that of any of the other 8-chromosome species. Like *glandulosa,* it occurs in sandy habitats. Such facts suggest that *septentrionalis* originally may have been a member of the genetic complex to which those two species belong. *Layia heterotricha* and *carnosa* are both able to cross with members of the 8-chromosome complex (fig. 55), but their hybrids are weak, have unpaired chromosomes, and are completely sterile; *heterotricha* is a fairly rare species from muddy flats in the inner Coast Range, where it occurs with the 7-chromosome *Munzii*. *L. carnosa* is a rare dwarf species of coastal sand dunes which grows in isolated local areas (fig. 57).

Within each of the species, the races and forms are interfertile, as exemplified particularly by the 14 intraspecific hybrids between contrasting races and populations within the species *Layia platyglossa* (fig. 35, p. 88). At the next level of evolution we find that hybrids between species belonging to the same species complex are partially intersterile in various degrees. Finally, members of distinct species complexes are very difficult to cross, irrespective of whether or not the parents have the same number of chromosomes or a different number. There is practically no pairing between their chromosomes, and the hybrids are fully sterile except in the rare cases when the chromosomes of both parents are added together to produce self-perpetuating fertile amphiploids that behave as new species.

Sometimes members of distinct complexes produce hybrids that are exceedingly weak or even sublethal. It is evident in these cases that the parental genomes are physiologically incompatible and cannot combine to produce a viable hybrid.

By such means evolution has brought about various degrees of relationship, superimposing ecological, genetical, cytological, and morphological relationships of various ranks. Of these relationships, the ecological is an exacting one, and the members of any one complex that attains wide distribution have to occupy different ecological niches. Conversely, in any one habitat we may find as many as two or three species of *Layia* together, but these invariably belong to different species complexes. The evolution of complete genetic barriers, therefore, enables more species of the same genus to grow in a given area. The genetic and cytological relationships have resulted in this kind of grouping of the species. The morphological differences may or may not accompany either ecological, genetical, or cytological distinctness, but fortunately for the taxonomist, there is usually enough correlation so that the various groups can be fairly readily identified.

The homology of the chromosomes is a criterion of relationship of relatively high order. The species complex is usually composed of a group with essentially homologous chromosomes and is roughly comparable to a section of a genus, or even a subgenus. The evolution of sets of chromosomes that are so different that they are unable to pair with each other represents a major stage in evolutionary differentiation above that of merely developing sterility barriers. These normal evolutionary steps can be obscured, however, if a repatterning of the chromosomes has taken place through inversions or translocations of segments. There is no evidence in the behavior of the chromosomes of the interspecific hybrids of *Layia* that repatterning of the chromosomes has been active in the evolution of its species as it has in the genus *Holocarpha* of the same subtribe.

Those morphological characters which are of taxonomic significance are fairly closely linked with the genetic systems that determine compatibilies between the units within the genus. Because of this linkage, they become important labels for recognizing the species and other major groups. Taxonomic characters have no intrinsic biological value to the plant groups except in so far as they are linked with the genetic-physiologic system that separates one species from another. It is the task of the taxonomist to recognize the characters of such significance.

Layia is an excellent example of a genus in various stages in evolutionary differentiation. Each species consist of a number of variable populations, and in some of the species these populations aggregate themselves into ecological races or ecotypes that are fitted for different environments. The evolution of moderate barriers to interbreeding in such a series of races evidently results in the development of groups of closely related species, the ecospecies of one species complex. In ecospecies of one complex the partial genetic barriers to free interbreeding are augmented by an ecological barrier.

Ecologic and genetic separations exist in all grades, including barriers that become so strong that interchange of genes is no longer possible. At this stage the chromosomes have also become nonhomologous and are unable to conjugate. Groups of species thus separated form distinct species complexes; they become distinct cenospecies. At an even more advanced stage, the species have become so distinct that the hybrid is much weaker than its parent species, or the species are unable to produce a viable hybrid, indicating that even the unbroken sets of parental genes do not fit together. We are then close to evolutionary discontinuities comparable to those which character-ize distinct genera. Within the confines of a genus, the species are linked together in a reticulate network, whereas distinct genera are more independent from each other, and may be compared with branches on a tree.

Fig. 58. Inflorescences of two *Madia* species and their hybrid. *Left,* M. *capitata,* $n = 16$, self-fertile. *Right,* M. *elegans,* $n = 8$, self-sterile. *Center,* their F_1 hybrid.

Isolated species in the genus Madia— The genus that morpholog-ically and genetically is most closely related to *Layia* is *Madia.* All Madias have entire leaves, whereas all Layias have divided or den-tate leaves. Morphologically, *Madia* is divided into several groups. The one that is closest to *Layia* consists of small, exclusively spring-flowering annuals which may have pappus on the akenes of the disk florets. *Madia nutans* and *Rammii* (fig. 50, p. 117) belong to this group. Another group of species consists of spring-, summer-, and fall-blooming annuals which have no pappus. Figure 58 shows the inflorescences of two species of that group, namely, *Madia capitata* Nutt., a small-rayed, self-fertile species with 16 pairs of chromosomes, and *Madia elegans* Don, which has showy flowers, is self-sterile, and has only 8 pairs of chromosomes. Their sterile hybrid is in the center. Finally, there are two perennial species with pappus, *Madia Bolanderi* Gray and *madioides* (Nutt.) Greene, the former a native of mid-altitude forests in the Sierra Nevada, the latter of moist coastal forests.

The species of *Madia* are cytologically and genetically much more isolated from each other than are the Layias. The results of a cytogenetic investigation in the genus are summarized in the crossing polygon, figure 59. There are about seventeen or eighteen good species in *Madia,* and the chromosome numbers vary between 6 and 24 pairs. Most of the species of *Madia* can be linked together through hybrids, but these are sterile, and, moreover, many hybrids have unpaired, nonhomologous chromosomes. There is, therefore, usually only one species to a species complex in *Madia,* and we express this technically by saying that its cenospecies contain only one ecospecies, or that the genus is largely composed of monotypic cenospecies.

Those *Madia* hybrids that happen to be vigorous and have unpaired, nonhomologous chromosomes tend to produce amphiploids that are fertile, true-breeding, intermediate new species (Clausen, Keck, and Hiesey, 1945). The 17-paired amphiploid, *M. nutrammii,* arose by crossing the species *Madia nutans* with 9 and *Rammii* with 8 pairs of chromosomes. One polyploid complex in *Madia* probably evolved in this manner. It consists of seven species having 8, 16, and 24 pairs of chromosomes. The 24-paired native species *M. citrigracilis* Keck of the interior of northern California was resynthesized experimentally three times from hybrids between the 8-paired *M. citriodora* Greene and the 16-paired *M. gracilis* (Smith) Keck (Clausen, Keck, and Hiesey, 1945). A very rare 8-paired relict species, *Madia subspicata* Keck, of the foothills of the Sierra Nevada is probably one of the progenitors of this polyploid complex of *Madia* species, but other diploids seem to have been lost.

The Madias are almost exclusively species of California, but a few of them venture beyond the borders of the state, and one species, *M. chilensis* (Nutt.) Reiche, occurs only in Chile. The latter has 16 pairs of chromosomes, like *Madia sativa* Molina, which is native to the

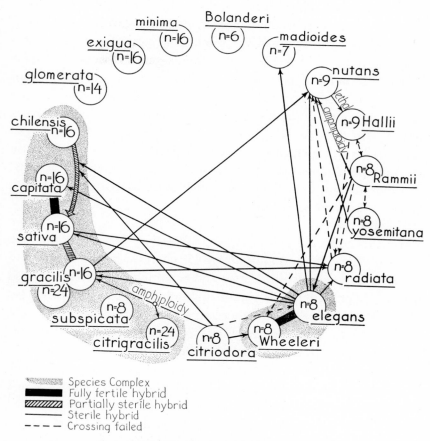

Fig. 59. Crossing polyglon of the genus *Madia*.

coastal regions of both California and Chile. *Madia chilensis* will cross with California *sativa,* but the hybrid is 95 per cent sterile. The chromosomes of the two species are nevertheless homologous, despite the great geographical distance and the evolutionary changes that must have taken place since *chilensis* became separated from its California relatives. Therefore, the only truly polyploid complex of the *Madiinae* has species both in California and in Chile, although the diploid progenitors of the complex appear to have been Californian.

Three species of *Madia* were previously considered to belong to other genera. *Madia nutans* (Greene) Keck was thought to be a *Layia,* but it crosses only with *Madia;* morphologically it is intermediate between the two genera. *Madia Wheeleri* (Gray) Keck was supposed to be a member of *Hemizonia,* a genus adjacent to *Madia,* but it was found to be completely interfertile with *Madia elegans* Don and it is definitely only a subspecies of the latter. *Hemizonella minima* Gray was thought to be a monotypic genus, but Dr. Keck found it to have the same chromosome number as *Madia exigua* (Smith) Gray, to which it is morphologically closely related, and it has now been renamed a *Madia.* In such instances the cytogenetic and morphologic criteria reinforce each other in making the genera more natural and acceptable.

Naturalness of the genera Layia and Madia— The naturalness of the two genera *Layia* and *Madia* is corroborated by the genetic evidence. The species within *Layia* and within *Madia* are interlinked through hybrids, but it is almost impossible to produce hybrids between the two genera. The only two known hybrids between them strengthen this conclusion, for they were characteristic of hybrids between very remotely related species. One hybrid between a 7-paired *Layia platyglossa* and an 8-paired *Madia elegans* was exceedingly weak. Another, between *Layia platyglossa* and a 16-paired *Madia sativa,* was produced in the wild and raised in the garden. This hybrid is shown in figure 60 between the parental strain of *Madia sativa* and the parental decumbent strain of *Layia platyglossa* from near Muir Beach, Marin County, California. Superficially this hybrid looked very much like the *Madia* and would probably have escaped notice in the wild, but it was completely sterile, had 23 chromosomes instead of 32 as in the *Madia,* and none of the chromosomes paired. None of the hybrid plants of this combination gave rise to amphiploids.

Layia and *Madia* constitute, therefore, two distinct crossing groups.

Within each of the two genera evolution is still reticulate, but the evolution within one does not now influence the other, for each follows its own pattern. Nevertheless, as geological periods go, the two genera probably branched off fairly recently from each other, because rare hybrids are still possible between the best mixers in both.

Fig. 60. A natural intergeneric hybrid between *Madia* and *Layia. Left, Madia sativa*, $n = 16$. *Right,* decumbent form of *Layia platyglossa*, $n = 7$. *Center,* their spontaneous hybrid, $2n = 23$. All grown in the Carnegie Institution garden at Stanford from seed gathered near Muir Beach, Marin County, California.

The genus Hemizonia, differentiated into sections— The subdivision of a large genus into separate subgroups or sections is exemplified by the genus *Hemizonia,* a neighbor of *Madia.* It consists of some 28 annual or perennial species, the former including both spring- and fall-blooming plants. They are native to the Coast Ranges and valleys of California and the adjacent islands.

The genus *Hemizonia* contains four sections, some of which are morphologically so distinct that they have been called genera. Figure 61 shows representatives of three of the sections. The section

Euhemizonia is represented by a spring- and a fall-blooming species, with their extremely vigorous hybrid between them, the section *Deinandra* by two species, and the section *Centromadia* by one. Finally, a hybrid between *Hemizonia ramosissima* Benth. and *H. Fitchii* Gray, combining the sections *Deinandra* and *Centromadia,* is shown.

The central plexus of the genus is the section *Deinandra,* which contains 12 species, having chromosome numbers from 9 to 13 pairs. As suggested by the crossing polygon, figure 62, the *Deinandra* section is bisected into natural groups, each of which consists of a series of relatively more closely related species that cover geographically different territory. One of these groups, the left half of section *Deinandra* as represented in figure 62, contains 6 species that bloom in the spring and early summer and have chromosome numbers ranging from 9 to 12. These species occur in pairs. One having 9 chromosomes consists of *H. Kelloggii* Greene of the Coast Range valleys and *H. pallida* Keck in the interior foothills. Another pair has 10 chromosomes, namely, *H. angustifolia* DC. (fig. 34, p. 85), which occupies a narrow strip along the coast, and *H. Halliana* Keck (fig. 1, p. 13), a very rare endemic remnant which was recently discovered in an alkaline mud flat in an otherwise dry valley of the Coast Range. These two species from contrasting environments are very different in gross morphology but are similar in floral characters, and the moderate fertility of their hybrid suggests a fairly close genetic relationship despite the effective geographic separation. A third pair, *H. mohavensis* Keck with 11 and an undescribed species, *H. arida,* with 12 chromosomes, are very rare desert species. They have been collected only once, and it is doubtful whether they still exist. They appear to have been stranded in unhospitable habitats far from close relatives.

Most of these species pairs appear to have originated as ecological races of wider distribution. *Hemizonia angustifolia* and *Halliana,* the only species of the entire subtribe with 10 pairs of chromosomes, must have had a wider distribution with interconnecting variation before the Coast Ranges arose and separated them in early Quaternary. This event doubtless desiccated the interior valleys and flats, but *Halliana* managed to find one refuge. It will be recalled from

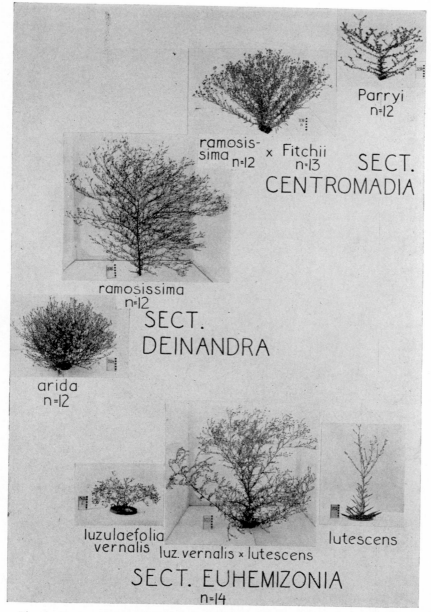

Parryi
n=12

ramosis-
sima n=12   x   Fitchii
                    n=13   SECT.
                           CENTROMADIA

ramosissima
n=12
          SECT.
       DEINANDRA

arida
n=12

luzulaefolia
vernalis   luz. vernalis x lutescens   lutescens

SECT. EUHEMIZONIA
n=14

Fig. 61. Representatives of five species in three sections of the genus *Hemizonia*, and two hybrids, one intrasectional, one intersectional.

Chapter VI that these events were thought also to have disrupted *Holocarpha macradenia* and *virgata,* except that in that case it was the coastal element of the group that disappeared.

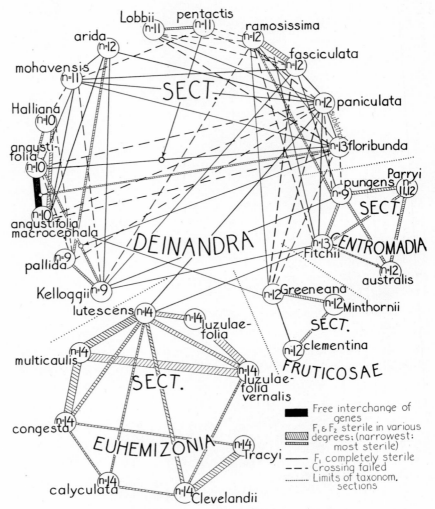

Fig. 62. Crossing polygon of the genus *Hemizonia.*

The other half of the *Deinandra* section have 11 to 13 pairs of chromosomes, and they are genetically so well separated from the first half that members of the two often occur together. One group of four young budding species, *Lobbii* (Greene) and *pentactis* (Keck) with 11 and *ramosissima* Benth. and *fasciculata* Torr. et Gray with 12 pairs of chromosomes, are vicarious in distribution through the Coast Ranges and valleys south of San Francisco Bay. The vicarious distribution suggests that they originated as ecological races of one species. Their partially fertile hybrids and their similar morphology strengthen this impression. The remaining two species of section *Deinandra, paniculata* Gray with 12 and *floribunda* Gray with 13 pairs of chromosomes, are genetically so well separated from the former group of four species that their distributions overlap.

A very different pattern of speciation has been evolved in the section *Euhemizonia,* the hayfield tarweeds of central California. The species of the section *Deinandra* differ in chromosome numbers and have strong barriers to interbreeding, but in contrast the Euhemizonias have evolved about 8 species, all having 14 pairs of chromosomes and being genetically closely enough related to permit a limited exchange of genes. This section constitutes a single complex of species that are highly drought-resistant and densely covered with exuding glands. The hayfield tarweeds are able to develop after the grasses have dried up in late spring. They continue to grow throughout the dry and hot summer until the late fall, and usually do not bloom before August. The various species of this section occupy habitats that are ecologically different, and they seldom overlap in distribution. They intercross easily, but the hybrids are partially sterile and the second generations are weak. Although these genetic barriers prevent the free interchange of genes (fig. 48, p. 114), their chromosomes are nevertheless homologous and able to pair with each other. This section of *Hemizonia* is the one that morphologically is closest to *Madia,* but none of its members have ever been known to cross with any species of *Madia* despite the numerous opportunities given to them in the Carnegie experiments.

A third section of the genus *Hemizonia, Centromadia,* is composed of four species with 9, 11, 12, and 13 pairs of chromosomes. Its species intercross almost as easily as those of *Euhemizonia,* although, like the Deinandras, they differ in chromosome number. The Centromadias also are fall-blooming and stay green during the dry California summers, but they do so by reducing their summer leaves to small, green, tough spines, hence their common designation as spike-weeds. Like the Euhemizonias, they are weeds of grain- and hay-fields, and species of these two sections may occur together because they are genetically very effectively isolated from each other.

The most common species of the *Centromadia* section is the 9-chromosome *Hemizonia pungens* (Hook. et Arn.) Torr. et Gray, which has developed three distinct race complexes, namely, one around San Francisco Bay, another in the interior valleys and south-ward, and a third in southern California. Hybrid intermixtures oc-cur in the passes where these subspecies meet. *Hemizonia Parryi* Greene was previously considered to be a subspecies of *pungens,* but its races have 11 and 12 pairs of chromosomes as compared with 9, it differs by having pappus on the disk florets, and its hybrids with *pungens* are fairly highly sterile. By contrast, the 11- and 12-chromosome races of *Parryi* intercross completely freely and pro-duce large and vigorous second generations, one of the few instances where a difference in chromosome number does not provide a ge-netic barrier. *H. Parryi* covers approximately the same territory as *pungens* and has developed parallel interfertile races. The southern California form of *Parryi,* however, has evolved into a distinct, al-though closely related, entity hitherto unrecognized as a species, *australis* (Keck), which is only partially interfertile with 12-chromosome forms of *Parryi* from central California. *Hemizonia Fitchii* Gray is the fourth of this section. It is the species most fiercely armed with sharp spines, has 13 pairs of chromosomes, and inhabits the interior valleys and foothills. Genetically it is the most isolated of the Centromadias, but it will cross as frequently with *Euhemizonia* and *Deinandra* as with members of its own section. These hybrids are completely sterile, however. For example, no good seeds were found among 13,000 empty ones harvested on seven individuals of *H. lutescens* × *Fitchii.* An equally sterile hybrid of *H. Kelloggii* × *Fitchii* was found in the wild; these parent species had 9 and 13 pairs of chromosomes, respectively, and the hybrid had 22 unpaired ones.

The section *Centromadia* is sometimes treated as a genus distinct from *Hemizonia* on account of its many striking morphological differences, but the existence of vigorous intersectional hybrids, both in the wild and in the experiment garden, indicates that *Centromadia* belongs within *Hemizonia*. In fact, the 9-chromosome *Hemizonia pungens* and the 12-chromosome *ramosissima* of the *Deinandra* section cross spontaneously (fig. 62), and their hybrids are so fertile that they can produce a small, strongly segregating F_2 population. It is evident, therefore, that the striking morphological differences between these two sections are biologically not as deep-seated as they appear to be.

The fourth section, *Fruticosae,* of the genus *Hemizonia* is a small group of low, perennial half-shrubs of the islands along the coast of southern and Baja California and of the adjacent mainland. These all have 12 pairs of chromosomes and are partially interfertile among themselves, but their hybrids with species of the *Deinandra* section are sterile. The presence of such hybrids, however, suggests that the *Fruticosae* belong to the genus *Hemizonia*.

The organization of *Hemizonia* suggests, therefore, that the genus is beginning to break apart, for the species within the four sections are fairly closely knit together, whereas the species belonging to different sections are only loosely attached. The sections have most of the earmarks of distinct genera, for characteristic and distinct patterns have been followed in the evolution of their component species. The existence of intersectional hybrids clearly indicates, however, that the whole genus is an evolutionary unit by itself.

The genus Viola, exploiter of a floral pattern— *Viola* was one of the first genera to be subjected to experimental investigations on evolution. It was only two or three years after the rediscovery of Mendel's laws that Ezra Brainerd started the investigations that led to his papers (1904, 1906 a, b) on natural hybrids between North American violets. He pointed out that some of the taxonomists' species were no more than races and that others were outright interspecific hybrids.

An example from Brainerd's papers of the kind of segregation that occurs among the offspring of natural *Viola* hybrids is seen in figure 63. It illustrates segregation in leaf characters in offspring of the

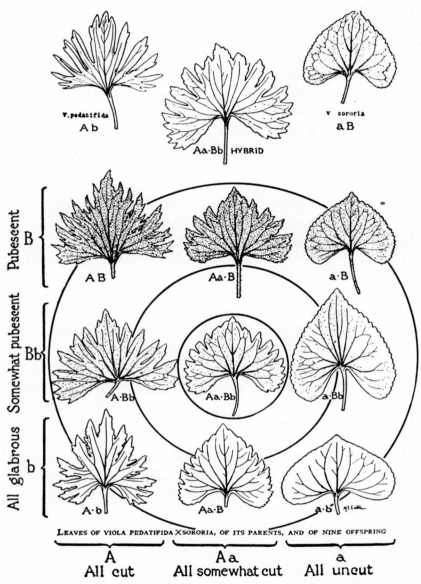

Fig. 63. Leaves of *Viola pedatifida, V. sororia,* their F_1 hybrid, and segregating F_2 offspring. (After E. Brainerd, 1924, courtesy Vermont State Agricultural Experiment Station.)

hybrid *Viola pedatifida* Don and *V. sororia* Nutt. This hybrid was described by Brainerd in 1913 and accompanied by a plate showing the segregated types. Figure 63 is from his review paper on violet hybrids of North America (Brainerd, 1924). The relatively simple segregation for the two characters of leaf cut and pubescence is clearly shown in this figure. Other characters that distinguish the parent species and were segregated in the hybrids were green as compared with purple color of capsule and buff versus brown color of seeds. In all characters except cut of leaves, *Viola sororia* was the dominant parent and one pair of genes appeared to be responsible for each of these differences.

The genus *Viola* appears to be the highest on the evolutionary scale of the *Viola* family, which consists largely of small trees and shrubs of tropical latitudes. The flowers of most of the genera of the family are built according to a radial pattern. The violets, on the other hand, are composed not only of small trees, shrubs, and woody cushion plants but also of perennial and annual herbs, and they have developed their characteristically bisymmetrical flowers which are different from the flowers of any other group of plants. Having evolved this floral pattern, the violets have exploited it and have developed many variations. The greatest variation in the floral pattern, specifically in the shape of the pistil and stigma, is found among the violets of the tropical latitudes, especially in the Andes of South America. Only 4 sections of the genus are represented at the northern temperate latitudes, and there are 7 sections at the tropical latitudes. Also, in the family as a whole, 14 of the 16 genera remained at tropical latitudes.

Suggestively enough, almost all the violets of the temperate latitudes are perennial or annual herbs and not shrubs like their relatives from tropical latitudes. It appears that after a few types had evolved that were physiologically capable of invading the temperate latitudes, these went on evolutionary sprees, multiplying their species around certain basic patterns, and fitting themselves into a great number of available ecological niches. These include the four sections *Chamaemelanium, Plagiostigma, Rostellatae,* and *Melanium.* The first three of these are still closely enough related so that species belonging to different sections are able to cross and produce an F_1. Such intersectional *Viola* hybrids are highly sterile and often very weak. On the other hand, the European pansies of the *Melanium* section are completely unable to cross with members of the other sections, although the pansies are extremely tolerant to interspecific crossing. Gershoy (1934) has shown that the growth of the pollen of the wild pansy, *Viola tricolor* L., is strongly inhibited in stigmas of the species of the other sections, so that it grows only a fraction of a millimeter in 100 hours or more.

The violets of the Northern Hemisphere have used the evolutionary device of developing series of species characterized by multiples of several basic chromosome numbers. Table 8 summarizes the chromo-

Table 8. Summary of chromosome numbers in the genus *Viola* (based on research by Miyaji, Gershoy, and Clausen).

Section Chamaemelanium, 6-series:

$n =$	6	12	18	24	30	36	
No. of species	16	11	2	5	—	1	Total, 35

Section Plagiostigma, subsections Stolonosae, Langsdorffianae, Adnatae, 12-series:

$n =$	12	24	36	48	
No. of species	32	6	2	1	Total, 41

  Subsection Blandae, $n = 22$, 2 species
  Subsection Boreali-Americanae, $n = 27$, 20 species
  Subsection Pedatae, $n = 28$, 1 species

Section Rostellatae, 10-series:

$n =$	10	20	30	40	
No. of species	26	7	—	1	Total, 34

Section Melanium, subsections Calcaratae, Cornutae, modified 10-series:

$n =$	10	11	20	30	
No. of species	3	3	2	1	Total, 9

  Subsection Tricolores, modified 6-series:

$n =$	7	8	12	13	17	18	24	
No. of species	1	1	1	2	3	1	2	Total, 11

Total number of *Viola* species investigated: 153

some numbers in 153 species of four sections of the genus, as they are reported by Miyaji (1913, 1929, 1930), Gershoy (1928, 1932, 1934), and Clausen (1922, 1926, 1927, 1929). Each of three of these sections of the genus has its own basic chromosome number, whereas the fourth has a tolerance to differences in chromosome number that is fairly unique among plants. The yellow-flowered species of the *Chamaemelanium* section of western North America and eastern Asia follow a series of multiples of 6 pairs, reaching to 36 pairs. The section *Plagiostigma,* a circumboreal group of meadow violets, follows a series of multiples of 12 pairs ending at 48 pairs. There are three groups of aberrants deviating from the 12-series in that section, namely, a group of two species with 22 pairs, a large complex of eastern North American stemless blue violets, all of which have 27 pairs, and an isolated species, *pedata* L., with 28 pairs. The section *Rostellatae,* the blue-flowered, stemmed violets of the North American and Eurasian continents, are characterized by species that have multiples of 10 pairs. Finally, in the *Melanium* section, to which the approximately 50 species of Europe, western Asia, northern Africa, and the eastern North American *V. Rafinesquii* Greene belong, there are hardly any multiple series at all, except that one group has species with chromosome numbers adjacent to multiples of 6 and another group has numbers adjacent to multiples of 10. Great differences in chromosome number do not prevent the species of this section from intercrossing, a situation that leads to considerable gene interchange.

The diagram in figure 64 is a summary of studies on interspecific hybridization in four sections of *Viola* carried on for a period of about 30 years on two continents. The crossing polygons in that diagram are based on the data reported by Brainerd (1906 and later), Gershoy (1928, 1932, 1934), and Clausen (1926, 1931b). In a few instances, where sufficiently detailed information was not available in Gershoy's papers for a classification into partially as compared with completely sterile hybrids, the diagram represents an estimate. Gershoy (1932) classified the hybrids as either sterile or fertile, sterile meaning at least 95 per cent failure of seed. In accordance with this criterion, most of the partially sterile hybrids between ecospecies of one cenospecies would be classified as fertile, although their fertility would be much less than that observed in hybrids between distinct races or subspecies within one ecospecies.

The crossing polygon in the upper left corner of figure 64 is based exclusively on Brainerd's early paper (1906b) of natural and garden-grown hybrids between the eastern stemless violets of the 27-chromosome group *Boreali-Americanae* of the section *Plagiostigma.*

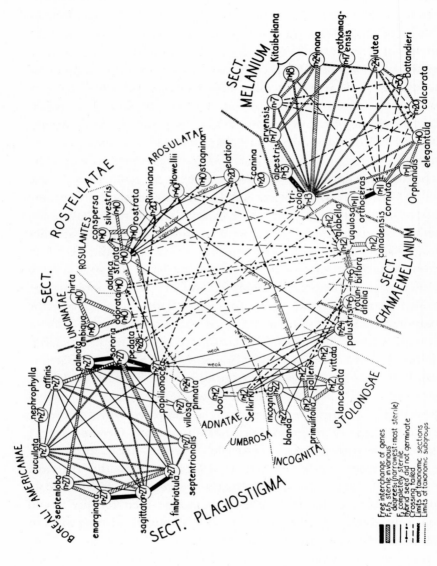

Fig. 64. Crossing polygon of the genus *Viola.*

All of these species have weak barriers to interbreeding, but the genetic barriers are fortified by ecological separation. When modern man cleared the forests, some of the external barriers to migration were removed, and these species came together and crossed and wiped out the distinctions between some of the earlier so-called species.

The data on the intrasectional crossings within *Plagiostigma, Rostellata,* and *Chamaemelanium* are based on Gershoy's investigations. His data indicate that the species within each of these sections arrange themselves into smaller subgroups of more closely related species that are connected together by hybrids that are only partially intersterile. Most of these subgroups, such as *Stolonosae, Incognitae, Uncinatae,* and *Rosulantes,* were recognized independently through morphological characters by taxonomists before the genetic data were available. These subgroups of closely related species are, in turn, more remotely connected with each other through sterile hybrids.

The hybrids between members of the different sections of *Viola* are difficult to produce; many attempts are failures, and others result in seeds with embryos that are unable to germinate, so that the F_1 plant is not seen. Some result in weak or dwarf F_1 hybrids. There are only two instances of vigorous intersectional hybrids, but these were sterile. No intersectional hybrids involving the *Melanium* section were produced, the pollen being unable to grow fast enough on the foreign stigma. This latter section is therefore both genetically and morphologically more sharply separated than are the others; it forms a comparium by itself, and the other three sections together form another comparium.

Within the section *Melanium* itself, the species constitute a plexus having weak genetic barriers fortified by ecological barriers similar to those found in the *Boreali-Americanae* of section *Plagiostigma.* The European *Melanium* pansies differ, however, from the North American stemless blue violets in that almost each species of the *Melanium* pansies has a different chromosome number. Also, in the pansies even species that differ in their number of chromosomes can produce hybrids that are moderately fertile. A great deal of interbreeding is still taking place in the wild between the pansy species, but this is not so extensive as to submerge the species completely, because the parental species are more vigorous than are the hybrid derivatives.

Figure 65 shows as an example the extensive segregation of flower characters in a second-generation hybrid between *Viola arvensis* Murr., an annual species with small, yellowish-white petals, and *rothomagensis* Desf., a perennial species with large purple petals, both of the *Melanium* section (Clausen, 1931b). Both have 17 pairs of chromosomes, but the original cross can be performed only by using *arvensis* as the maternal parent; the reciprocal combination always produces shriveled seeds. The $17 + 17$ chromosomes in the F_1 hybrid form 10 to 12 pairs, the remainder of the chromosomes being unpaired, or associating in strings of three to four chromosomes. The hybrid is nevertheless able to produce 250 to 450 fairly viable seeds per individual, and an F_2 population of more than 500 individuals was obtained. In figure 65 a flower of the small-petaled F_1 is shown between the flowers of the two parental species in the topmost row, and the next four rows show examples of the segregated types in the extremely variable F_2. The range of segregation includes forms approaching the parental species in floral character and others with entirely new characters, such as some with deep, velvety upper petals and others with large, colored sepals or with spurs on the lateral petals also. Some of the latter forms may have arisen through the loss of chromosomes containing inhibiting genes, but segregations like these emphasize the point that there are still latent evolutionary possibilities within the *Melanium* section of the genus.

Figure 66 shows some of the variation in the flowers of six of the species of the *Melanium* section. In the top row are flowers of *V. Battandierii* W. Beckr. with 30, *lutea* Huds. with 24, and *rothomagensis* Desf. with 17 pairs of chromosomes. The last two flowers in the top row and all of those in the second row belong to various forms of *Viola tricolor* L., all having 13 pairs of chromosomes. In the bottom row are two forms of *Viola arvensis* Murr. with 17 pairs of chromosomes, followed by four forms of *V. Kitaibeliana* Roem. et Schult. with 7, 8, 18, and 24 pairs of chromosomes, respectively. This picture shows, on one hand, the great morphological variability combined

Fig. 65. Flowers of *Viola arvensis*, $n = 17$ (*top, left*), *V. rothomagensis*, $n = 17$ (*top, right*), their F_1 hybrid (*top, center*), and their segregating F_2 (*four lower rows*).

with constancy in chromosome number in the 13-paired *V. tricolor*, as compared with the morphological constancy and extreme cytological variability in the 7- to 24-paired *Kitaibeliana*, on the other. The forms in the row at the bottom are genetically the most dominant ones in the group, and the velvety black flower of *tricolor* in the center is the bottom recessive. There are at least 7 pairs of dominant genes suppressing this dark color before it becomes the inconspicuous yellowish white of *arvensis* or *Kitaibeliana*. The suppression of petal size is almost as complicated. The small species with the inconspicuous flowers are therefore gene pools from which much of the variation in this section could be derived simply by a loss of dominant

Fig. 66. Flowers of wild *Viola* species of the section *Melanium. Top row, from left:* V. Battandierii, $n = 30$; V. lutea, $n = 24$; V. rothomagensis, $n = 17$; two forms of V. tricolor alpestris, $n = 13$. *Center row:* five forms of V. tricolor, $n = 13$. *Bottom row, from left:* two forms of V. arvensis, $n = 17$; four forms of V. Kitaibeliana, namely, $n = 7$, $n = 8$, $n = 18$, and $n = 24$ (*nana*). (From Clausen, 1931b.)

genes, or even of whole chromosomes. Genetic data from the crossings indicate that the 24-chromosome *nana* form of *Kitaibeliana* in the lower right corner of figure 66 has considerable duplication in its four sets of chromosomes.

The data in figure 64 on crossability of three of the chromosome forms within *Kitaibeliana* indicate that the 7-, 18-, and 24-paired forms within that species are fairly highly intersterile, whereas the hybrid between 13-chromosome *tricolor* and 24-chromosome *Kitai-*

beliana nana is surprisingly fertile for species that chromosomally and morphologically are so different. Hybrid fertility is therefore not an unfailing guide to be used alone as a scale to determine degrees of relationship. It should be used in connection with all the other data available.

In the western part of the United States, with its varied topography, the *Chamaemelanium* section has built up a pyramid of species in multiples of 6 pairs of chromosomes. Probably most of the

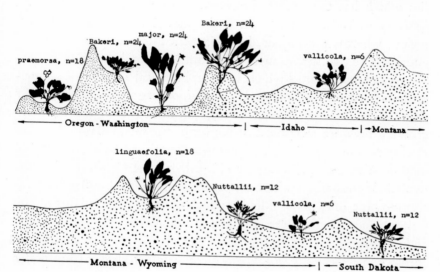

Fig. 67. Representatives of the various entities of the polyploid species complex of *Viola Nuttallii* on a profile of western North America at 45° N. latitude.

species of the higher stories of this pyramid have arisen by the addition of whole sets of chromosomes of very distinct species, followed by the doubling of the chromosomes which transformed the hybrids into fertile new species. In that manner the species have been compounded. Studies on this group of violets have been conducted by Professor Milo S. Baker of Santa Rosa Junior College and the writer. Some of these have been published (Baker, 1935, 1948, 1949), but most of the subspecies are still unpublished, although the descriptions are in manuscript form.

The species and other entities of each of the *Chamaemelanium* complexes occupy very different habitats, as exemplified by figure 67. This is a chart of the *Viola Nuttallii* complex, which is one of the approximately 10 groups or sub-sections of species belonging to the *Chamaemelanium* section of the genus *Viola* in western North America. Specimens of the various entities of the *Nuttallii* group are placed on a profile across the western United States at approximately 45° N. latitude from the Pacific coast to the Great Plains at those places where these particular entities occur geographically. The species which has the lowest chromosome number is the 6-paired *V. vallicola* A. Nels. of the Great Basin plateau in the intermountain region, whereas the 12-paired *V. Nuttallii* Pursh is a species of the prairies. The two species meet in certain areas, and the 18-paired entity *linguaefolia* Nutt., which in morphological characters is intermediate between *vallicola* and *Nuttallii,* occurs at somewhat higher altitudes in the Great Basin, although all three species can be found growing together near the east border of the Great Basin. Another 18-chromosome species, *V. praemorsa* Dougl., occupies the coastal strip of Washington, Oregon, and northernmost California, but the two 18-chromosome entities are separated from each other by a 24-chromosome one, *major* Hook., which grows on the plains of the Columbia and Snake rivers and also at mid-altitudes in the Cascades and the Sierra Nevada. In the Sierra Nevada there is also another 24-chromosome species, *Viola Bakeri* Greene, which differs from *major* in having a branched root crown and entire, ciliate leaves. It probably had a considerably different ancestry.

Figure 68 shows specimens of the *Viola purpurea* complex, also of the *Chamaemelanium* section, across a profile of the western United States at approximately 38° N. latitude from central California to Utah. The *purpurea* complex differs from the *Nuttallii* complex in having only two chromosome numbers represented, but its morphological variability is fully as great. The diploid 6-paired species covers the greatest part of the area, the 12-paired ones being more local; one of the latter occurs in the Coast Ranges and foothills of California, and the other as a fairly rare endemic in Utah. The first of these, the 12-paired *Viola quercetorum* Baker et Clausen, is a species of the oak savannahs ranging from the coast of California to approximately 3000 feet altitude in the western foothills of the Sierra Nevada. Where the Sierran coniferous forest replaces the oak savannahs, *quercetorum* is also replaced by the 6-paired *V. purpurea* Kell. As figure 68 indicates, there are two ecological subspecies of *purpurea* on the west side of the mountains, and there are two others on the east side at altitudes of from 6000 to 10,000 feet. The forms on the arid east side have their buds and rootstocks buried in sand soil,

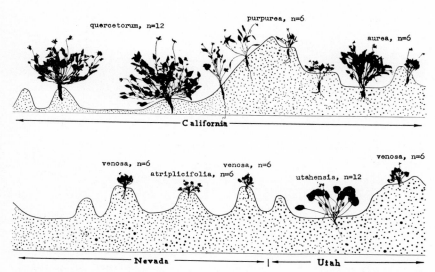

Fig. 68. Representatives of the various entities of the polyploid complex of *Viola purpurea* on a profile of western North America at 38° N. latitude.

and their stems above the ground are very much reduced. At lower altitudes in the desert regions of California and Nevada there is another entity, *V. aurea* Kell., which, like the others from this region, has the buds of the rootstocks buried in sand. On the higher ranges of the Great Basin plateau through Nevada to the Wasatch Range in Utah and northward to Montana there are other 6-chromosome entities of very short stature, namely, *venosa* Wats. and *atriplicifolia* Greene. On the plains in Utah there is a 12-paired local species, *V. utahensis* Baker et Clausen, which often is found in places where the 6-paired *venosa* and the 6-paired *vallicola* of the *Nuttallii* group meet, and it combines the morphological characteristics of both.

In this manner a large superstructure of polyploid species has been built on the approximately 10 basic groups of 6-paired species. Figure 69 depicts the more significant western North American species of the *Chamaemelanium* section at the proper chromosome levels and includes a few species from outside of this territory for comparison. Single lines along the lower rows of this diagram indicate artificial hybrids produced by Gershoy; one of these combines *Viola biflora* L.

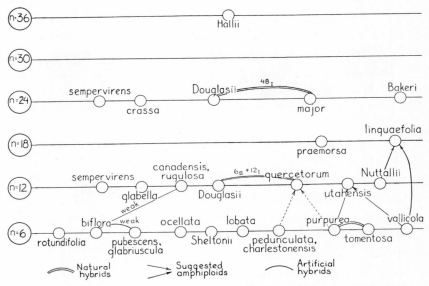

Fig. 69. Polyploid levels in the section *Chamaemelanium* of the genus *Viola*. See text.

with *rugulosa* Greene, and the other, *biflora* with *pubescens* Ait. The presence of these hybrids, together with the morphological similarity of the parent species, indicates that *biflora* more naturally belongs with the *Chamaemelanium* section, rather than in a section by itself, as has been formerly proposed. The vertical order of arrangement indicates the probable relationships between the entities at different polyploid levels. *Viola sempervirens* Greene, for example, exists both in a 12- and a 24-paired form, the former in central California, the latter in northern Oregon. Likewise, the 24-paired *V. crassa* Makino is a Japanese counterpart of the circumpolar 6-paired *biflora*. *Viola Douglasii* Steud. exists in both a 12- and a 24-paired form, the

differentiation, or more or less simultaneously in any two or three of these directions, all of these criteria for relationship are considered in figure 70. Genetic differentiation includes also chromosome differentiation. In the analysis depicted in this figure only the evolutionary entities within a single genus or within its experimental counterpart, the comparium, are being considered. It does not present the criteria for distinct comparia.

Mor- phology	Ecolo- gy	Genetic relationships		
		Hybrids fertile, second generation vigorous	Hybrids partially sterile, second generation weak	Hybrids sterile, or none
Morphologically distinct	In distinct environments	distinct subspecies (or ecotypes) of one species	distinct species (ecospecies)	distinct species complexes (cenospecies)
	In the same environment	local variations of one species	species overlapping in common territory	
Morphologically similar	In distinct environments	distinct ecotypes of one species	genetic species only (autoploidy or chromosome repatterning)	
	In the same environment	taxonomically the same entity		

Fig. 70. Analytical key to the evolutionary entities within the genus or the comparium.

Considering first morphologically distinct evolutionary entities as indicated in figure 70, distinct subspecies are either spatially or ecologically separated, but this is the only barrier to interbreeding they possess. Distinct species (or ecospecies) of one species complex occupy ecologically distinct environments, and their hybrids are partially sterile. Distinct species complexes (or cenospecies), on the other hand, are completely intersterile, and they may or may not occur in the same kind of environment. Only local variations (biotypes) of one species are involved where there are no barriers to interbreeding and the entities occur together, as in the case of *Layia chrysanthemoides* and *Calliglossa* discussed in Chapter V (p. 70–71), even though in this instance they previously were treated as distinct genera.

Among those evolutionary entities that are morphologically similar are the distinct ecotypes or ecological races of one species that occupy ecologically distinct environments. Gross genetic changes, as, for example, repatterning of the chromosomes or doubling of the chromosomes, may lead to the development of species that are genetic only. They may occur in the same or different environments, and may be fully or partially intersterile, as in the case of the genus *Holocarpha,* discussed in Chapter VI (pp. 105–107). They often lack some of the characteristics of full-fledged species.

At the point where groups of species are no longer able to intercross, they maintain themselves independently of each other and have become distinct comparia. We have discussed examples of such groups in the *Melanium* section of the genus *Viola* as compared with the comparium formed by the three sections *Chamaemelanium, Plagiostigma,* and *Rostellatae,* and also in the two distinct but related genera *Madia* and *Layia,* each of which constitutes such a comparium. The environment ceases to be of selectional significance in differentiating comparia except in so far as the composite ecology of the entire group may be affected.

These factors and forces cause the species and other evolutionary entities to arrange themselves into natural groups of various ranks and of various kinds. A more complete discussion and definition of these biosystematic units has previously been presented (Clausen, Keck, and Hiesey, 1945, pp. 63–66). The analysis outlined above is a relatively crude and oversimplified one, for all classification falls short of depicting the tremendous diversity in relationships observed among living organisms. Nevertheless, this kind of analysis is based upon criteria of basic significance in the evolution of organisms and does emphasize broad principles that lead to the recognition of corresponding stages of evolution in widely different groups of the plant kingdom.

VIII

The Physiologic-genetic Species Concept and the Dynamics of the Evolution of Species and Genera

ONE of the most important departures in the evolution of living things is the development of the species. During the last two chapters we have discussed the many ways and means by which species and even subgenera can become separated from each other. The separation, however, is the negative side of the species problem, and we should now consider what it takes to build a species that can function in a competitive world. Unfortunately, we do not know very much, as yet, about the details of what keeps a species together.

The nature of species— We have found that a species has an organization that is far more intricate than we could have guessed it to be. Take, as an example, the Achilleas or milfoils discussed in Chapter IV. Starting with the minimum of 11 physiologically distinct races found within a single transect 200 miles long that lies across central California, and extrapolating from there to the many climates and ecological niches from tropical to arctic latitudes that are occupied by Achilleas, one senses that the number of physiologically distinct races within this one group of plants may well run into the hundreds. Within the species *Achillea borealis* alone, the differences range between giant forms of the subtropical San Joaquin Valley to the tiny dwarfs on the peaks of the Aleutian Islands in the cold and stormy North Pacific. Figure 71 illustrates some of the differences between these contrasting races when both are grown together in the same garden at Stanford. The bars in the graph in the top part of the figure show the mean monthly amplitudes of temperature in a southern and a northern locality. These amplitudes are the differences between mean monthly maxima and mean monthly minima. The graphs are as presented by Clausen, Keck, and Hiesey (1948), and are based on the climatic data assembled by the United States Weather Bureau. The black bars indicate the monthly amplitudes at Fresno at 36° N. latitude, near the habitat of the San Joaquin Valley race, and the shaded bars indicate the monthly amplitudes at Seward on the southern coast of Alaska at 60° N. latitude. No climatic data are available from Kiska Peak at 52° N. latitude, in the center of the North Pacific, the habitat of the other plant illustrated, but the data from Seward may serve to show the general trend of the annual temperature difference between a southern and a northern latitude. However, Seward is doubtless more continental in character than is Kiska. The differences in temperature between the San Joaquin Valley and the habitat of the Kiska race are so striking that it is not so remarkable that the two races shown in figure 71 are very different.

It is not just this startling diversity that is so remarkable; even more, it is the realization that forms so different may still belong to the same species and are able to exchange their genes without upsetting the finely balanced genetic-physiologic systems. These two Achilleas from climates so contrasting and so far apart are still able to cross. They produce a vigorous hybrid which is highly fertile and from which we now have about 2000 healthy F_2 offspring growing in our gardens at Stanford. The parents obviously differ by many genes, each with a minor effect, but the compounded effect of all of them results in striking contrasts in morphology. There are probably invisible differences in physiology that are as striking as the morphological ones. Nevertheless, as long as one remains within the limits of this species, the genes from its various races can be interchanged without disturbing the fine internal mechanisms that keep its physiological processes in balance.

This same San Joaquin Valley *Achillea borealis* has also been crossed with a dwarfish race of *Achillea millefolium* from northern

Fig. 71. Contrasting ecological races of *Achillea borealis* from two highly different climates. *Left,* a plant from the San Joaquin Valley, California. *Right,* an alpine dwarf from Kiska in the Aleutian Islands. Both were grown in the garden at Stanford. *Top,* mean amplitudes in temperature for the twelve months of the year at Fresno, California, and at Seward, Alaska. (Adapted from Clausen, Keck, and Hiesey, 1948.)

Iceland, a species which has the same number of chromosomes as *borealis* and comes from a climate similar to that of the Aleutians. In this hybrid, however, something goes wrong with the mechanism of heredity, for the first-generation hybrid is fairly highly sterile, although it is vigorous. The sterility means that the genes of the two cannot be exchanged without upsetting the balance of two distinct genetic-physiologic systems. The result is somewhat analogous to what might happen if one were to try to exchange the gears of a Buick and an Austin.

If a plant is to survive, the first requirement is that there must be developmental balance in its organization, so that the various tissues and organs can develop properly at the right time. Likewise, its numerous physiological processes must be synchronized. For example, the plant must be able to produce more food by assimilation than it burns in respiration. The entire delicate physiological system, governed by an equally intricate system of genes, must form a workable unit. We can sum this up by stating that the genes of the plant should form a harmonious combination, so that the physiological processes managed by the genes result in normal development.

Physiological processes, as, for example, assimilation and respiration, are changed in rate with temperature, but they may not change in the same degree. The range of environments for which a race is adapted depends probably to a considerable extent upon the temperature levels at which its rate curves for assimilation and respiration cross each other. Although very little is known about this phase of race metabolism, success obviously will be achieved only within the range of temperatures where a given race produces more food than it burns up. The upper and lower levels of positive assimilation probably vary from one climatic race to the next.

We do not know much about the mechanisms by which genetic systems govern the physiological processes, but they are probably similar to the ones that determine differences in morphology. We can then expect to find, for example, series of genes that increase assimilation at a given temperature, balanced against others that may slow the process down. Climatically contrasting races within one species are still able through crossing to exchange genes without upsetting the internal developmental balance in such gene systems. The results obtained from crossing foothill and subalpine races of *Potentilla glandulosa* indicate that the exchange of genes between climatically contrasting races of one species can produce individuals that are able to fit other environments and develop normally there.

Within a given species there probably is a basic genetic-physiologic balance which is not disturbed so long as one crosses only races within that species. Each species has evolved its own kind of genetic-physiologic system, and the systems of some species are so successfully balanced that very marked variations of them can be developed that are able to fit contrasting climates.

The kind of segregations one obtains after intercrossing species and races of various degrees of distinctness suggests that both the balanced development of the species and its fitness to the series of environments it occupies are achieved through genetic systems operating through the physiology. These systems differ from one species to another, and they can evolve either through gradual small changes in a great number of genes, each gene having a minor but cumulative effect, or through more abrupt changes either in the organization of the individual chromosomes or in the total number of chromosomes. The latter methods represent short cuts to speciation.

A considerable part of the apparent present-day discontinuity between species probably arose as intermediate species disappeared. In such a manner, gradual transitions were replaced by discontinuities. Neither ecological races nor species seem to be completely continuous in their variation, and there is a far from infinite number of gene systems in existence. The discontinuities probably exist because relatively few combinations can actually be successful in satisfying the exacting demands of the internal functions and also the demands of fitness to the external environment.

Means of producing variability— Evolution depends upon the dynamic equilibrium between two opposing forces: one is the constant enrichment of variability, and the other is selection among this variation. Selection alone is useless in evolution unless new variation is constantly being produced. The organization of living organisms in general is such that the capacity to produce variation is preserved. We should, therefore, consider the sources of variability.

The chart in figure 72 summarizes the various sources of varia-

Building blocks	Type of process and source of variability	Evolution-ary level
Genes	CREATIVE: Gene mutations RECOMBINATION: Independent assortment of genes and crossing-over LOSS: Deletion of genes	Intra-specific
Chromo-some seg-ments	RECOMBINATION: Repattern-ing of chromosomes by in-versions and translocations DUPLICATION: Duplication of chromosome segments LOSS: Loss of chromosome segments	Intra- or inter-specific
Chromo-somes	RECOMBINATION: Indepen-dent assortment of un-changed chromosomes DUPLICATION: Duplication of whole chromosomes LOSS: Loss of whole chromo-somes	
Genomes	DUPLICATION: Autoploidy, duplication of whole genomes ADDITION: Amphiploidy, addi-tion of different genomes	Inter-specific

Fig. 72. Sources of genetic variability and the means of producing it.

bility and the processes through which variations arise. These proc-esses may use as building blocks either the individual gene, segments of chromosomes, whole chromosomes, or whole sets of chromosomes. Essentially, there are three kinds of processes going on, namely, creative, recombining, and deleting processes. Duplication and addition are essentially but variants of recombination.

Variability affecting single genes produces intraspecific variability. At the opposite end of the scale, the addition of whole, distinct genomes results in new and distinct species. What happens to the individual chromosomes or segments of chromosomes may be of either intra- or interspecific significance. Direct duplication of a set of chromosomes neither produces anything new nor changes the balance relations between the genes. Autoploidy is therefore usually intraspecific, unless the new autoploid happens to fit a different environment, in which case differential selection will soon make the autoploid different from its undoubled parent. Having acquired barriers to interbreeding, as well as morphological and ecological distinctness, autoploids thus can become distinct species.

The only evolutionary process that brings something new into existence is gene mutation, the process by which new genes are produced, either to be rejected through selection or to be incorporated into an already existing gene system.

Recombination works with all the various building blocks available and tests them in all kinds of patterns. The finest and most resilient genetic structure of a species develops through the recombination of very many genes with minute effects, but this is the result of a very slow building process. Losses and deletions are radical innovations that are very demanding upon the species. It requires a genetically well-buffered initial balance between the genes of a system to tolerate losses. Those species which have pyramided their building through repeated additions of whole genomes are better able to tolerate losses than are species on the diploid level.

Actually, we do not know very much about the nature of the processes that produce variability. Despite intensive research along these lines, we do not as yet know whether some of the mutations are the result of changes in side chains of big organic molecules, or of the addition of a molecule at a definite point on the chromosome, or of some other molecular change. If it is either one of these, we should probably list gene mutation as another form of recombination on the molecular level.

We do not even know much about the nature of the circumstances that result in crossing over, whereby a block of genes changes position from one chromosome to its partner. The real causes of chromosome repatterning through translocation of segments between nonhomologous chromosomes, or through inversions of segments, also remain as secrets, together with the general problem of the nature of the chromosomes and why they pair in the first place.

Fig. 73. Evolution through crossing in *Viola tricolor* and *V. arvensis. Left half,* flowers of *V. tricolor, n* = 13, and *arvensis, n* = 17, and three derived new forms below, namely, *V. hyperchromatica, n* = 22, *V. petaloidea, n* = 14, and a segregated *arvensis* with *n* = 16, one chromosome less than the parental *arvensis. Right half,* two forms of *V. arvensis,* both with *n* = 17, and a new form that arose in hybrid progeny of the two. The new form has lost one pair of chromosomes and has therefore only 16 pairs, but it has gained in color and size of petals. (From Clausen, 1931b.)

The loss of single chromosomes is probably one of the simplest evolutionary processes, and its effect cautions us in the use of phrases such as "progressive evolution" and other clichés. A case in *Viola arvensis* (Clausen, 1931b) which is illustrated in figure 73 is very revealing, because the genetic backgrounds of this species and of its close relative, *Viola tricolor,* are well known. Two strains of *Viola arvensis* collected within a distance of 6 miles of each other were crossed; the flowers of these strains are shown to the right in figure 73. There was incomplete pairing in the hybrid and one of the 17 chromosome pairs of this species was lost in some of the progeny, resulting in a 16-paired form. This loss led to a gain in both size and color of the flower. From crossing experiments it is known that the small-flowered *V. arvensis* possesses 7 pairs of progressively inhibiting genes for black flower color, plus suppressors governing petal size. The chromosome which carries the suppressors both for velvety color in the upper petals and for petal size was lost, resulting in what might be called a new species, having one chromosome less than its parents and a chromosome number not known in any other species of *Viola*. The new 16-paired form remained constant through eight generations from the hybridization. Wild species appear to contain rich pools of genes, the actions of which are suppressed by inhibitors, as in this example. Not knowing the background, one would be inclined to list this loss of a pair of chromosomes with all its genes as an example of "progressive evolution."

The left half of figure 73 illustrates other ways in which constant new forms can arise among the pansies of Europe. To the extreme left is *Viola tricolor,* with 13 pairs of chromosomes, which was crossed with the 17-paired *arvensis*. Three new constant forms that arose among the offspring of this cross are shown below the parent species. To the right among these three is a new constant *arvensis* similar to its *arvensis* parent except that it has 16 pairs of chromosomes instead of 17. It was not the chromosome containing suppressing genes, however, that disappeared, as in the former example with the large, velvety petals. These two 16-paired segregants, therefore, are morphologically very different. Another constant offspring had 14 pairs of chromosomes, and had gained large, showy sepals colored like petals, a character not found in any other *Viola*. This character also probably arose through the loss of a suppressor gene. The third constant offspring of this cross, to the extreme left, arose through the duplication of some of the unpaired chromosomes, resulting in an increase in chromosome number over that of both parents, namely, to 22 pairs, instead of 13 or 17 pairs.

This series of examples of some of the evolutionary processes at work in the species complex of the wild pansies emphasizes the fact that we actually know very little about the physiological effect of even such processes as loss and recombination of whole chromosomes.

Selection— The sources of variability we have just discussed will constantly produce new variants from which to select. Baur (1924) and Tammes (1925) found that some of these differences are so slight that it requires special care in observation to prove that they exist. Genetic variation produces the working capital of evolution, and selection sifts the investments. Without constant variability, selection would soon run out of risk capital to start new ventures.

Selection is twofold. Each change has to pass the test of several selective stages. The first of these stages is the *internal selection* which takes place in the organism in which the change arose. If the new gene or the new combination of genes is not intercompatible with the genes already incorporated into the genetic system of the species, it will be rejected unless modifiers arise which ameliorate the effect of the newcomer. If the new gene or gene arrangement disturbs the proper timing of the physiological and growth processes in the organism in which it arose, it will be selected against and will disappear. Physiologically poorly balanced recombinations between genes from different gene systems will likewise be discarded, some in the gametic stage as sterile pollen and aborted ovules, others as unbalanced zygotes at some stage after fertilization has taken place. The main biological function of a species is to store in dynamic equilibrium a workable balance of genes.

In the second stage of selection, the variability is subject to *external selection* by the environment so that, for example, the rhythm of the individual fits the seasonal and diurnal periodicities of the environment, the soil and light conditions, and other factors. Unfit combinations will thereby disappear even though they may successfully have passed the tests of internal selection. Each individual must meet both sets of requirements, and the species and races are the products of such selection within geologic periods.

The evolution of barriers to interbreeding which isolate species and other biological categories of higher order is incidental to the creative and recombining processes which produce the materials on which selection works. Such barriers merely separate individuals into breeding groups, whereas the creative, recombining, and selective processes incorporate the variability into the genetic system of the species and fit its individuals and races to their respective environments.

	F_1		F_2	Hybrid generations possible	Genetic classification of parents
High crossability	vigorous	fully fertile	vigorous, healthy	$F_1 + F_2$ at least	same ecospecies
			weak, unhealthy, or dwarfed		distinct eco-species of one cenospecies
		partially fertile	vigorous, healthy		
			weak, unhealthy, or dwarfed		
Low crossability	weak	sterile	amphiploids possible	F_1 only	distinct ceno-species of one comparium
		sterile	none		
	sublethal				
No crossability	dies in embryonic stage			none	distinct comparia
	pollen able to stimulate selfing in the species to be crossed				
	pollination has no effect				

Fig. 74. Stages in the development of genetic incompatibility.

Stages in genetic incompatibility— Figure 74 outlines the various stages in the development of genetic incompatibility. In figure 72 were considered the various stages involved in assembling the gene material into gene blocks, whole chromosomes, and whole sets of chromosomes. In figure 74 we consider the stages from high to low crossability, and to no crossability. These stages in evolution may or may not be directly related to the chromosomal situation. The significance of the vigor and fertility of the first-generation hybrids is also considered, as are the vigor and the health of the second generation, the number of hybrid generations possible, and the evolutionary stage of the entities being tested. This chart refers solely to genetic incompatibilities, with no consideration at all of ecological and morphological distinctness or of the chromosome situation, except in so far as it is implied by the genetic compatibilities.

It will be noticed that the category at the top is the only one in which no breakdown occurs after hybridization, but where gene exchange can go on indefinitely. Natural entities that are thus able freely to exchange their genes belong to one ecospecies. In the next category down the line, the breakdown in interfertility does not begin to appear before the second generation, but in the following categories it is noticeable in the first generation. The F_1's, however, are still vigorous, and the initial crossing is easy. Entities separated in these patterns are closely related species of one species complex, or are distinct ecospecies of one cenospecies.

In the next major step the F_1 is sterile but still vigorous. Cytologically, this category includes a long series of stages of evolutionary differentiation from those in which the chromosomes of the parents are completely homologous to those in which the chromosomes are completely nonhomologous. The latter category and also some of those with partially homologous chromosomes may give rise to new constant species by chromosome doubling in the sterile F_1. In this manner a species arises that breeds as a double organism; that is, it is composed of the inheritances of both of its parent species. Some of the parents of amphiploids may have low initial crossability, but their F_1's will always be vigorous. We have now entered into the stage where only the F_1 is possible, because the amphiploids perpetuate the F_1 type without segregation. At this stage the parents have become distinct cenospecies or species complexes. No interchange of genes between them is possible, although their genomes have been added.

At the next three stages of low initial crossability, even the original gene combinations of the parents do not fit together, and the F_1 either is weak or dies soon after germination. In the last of these stages, the new hybrid dies in the embryonic stage and the initial hybrid seeds are not even able to germinate.

Certain species are so remotely related that no hybrid can ever be formed between them, but there are transitional stages in which the pollen is able to stimulate self-pollination in otherwise self-sterile species. The ability to induce self-pollination disappears when the species belong to different families, and usually even when they belong to different genera. In such stages of genetic incompatibility, where not even a first-generation hybrid is possible, we say that the species belong to different *comparia*, for we cannot even obtain an F_1. This stage of genetic differentiation is fairly comparable to that of the distinct genera of orthodox taxonomy.

The chart just discussed might seem to be a very complex one, but it represents actually a great oversimplification of the real situation that exists among the various stages of differentiation in living plants. Each of the categories in the chart should actually be subdivided into many, but it would then become so complex that it would be difficult to grasp its meaning. Also, one would have to superimpose on the genetic incompatibilities the chromosomal, ecological, and morphological differentiation of the entities. In so doing, one would get an impression of the complexity in the organization of living things. At this point we realize the magnitude of the task of the taxonomists in classifying and naming the entities in a system of living things as intricate as this.

Isolating mechanisms— The chart in figure 75 represents an attempt to classify the kinds of isolating mechanisms that operate in the various stages of speciation. In the left-hand column of this chart we find listed the degrees and modes of separation of entities; in the next two columns are shown their effects in the F_1's and F_2's of the hybrids between such races and species; and in the last two columns are listed the isolating barriers that are operative.

The first four categories of separation are intraspecific, and the genes of the parental genomes are freely interchangeable after crossing. The top category is the one with the least separation, namely, the kind of separation that exists between local populations of the same kind of ecological zone. Such a separation is based exclusively on distance.

An extreme example of isolation solely by distance is known from populations of *Capsella bursa-pastoris* (L.) Moench, the shepherd's purse. There are diploid, 8-paired species in this complex, but we are concerned only with the tetraploid, 16-paired group, which is native to Europe but has been introduced as weeds all over the world, including western North America. After having cultivated and crossed strains of *bursa-pastoris* and relatives received from both

Degree and mode of separation	F_1	F_2	Type of barriers	
PARENTAL GENOMES FREELY INTERCHANGE GENES: (1) Geographic separation only	vigorous	vigorous	spatial, but non-ecologic	external only
(2) Selective pollination by different agents (3) Climatic or edaphic separation (4) Different time of flowering	vigorous	vigorous	ecologic	external and internal
PARENTAL GENOMES RECOMBINE BUT OFFSPRING WEAK OR INVIABLE: (5) F_1 fertile, but F_2 weak (zygotic sterility) (6) F_1 partially sterile and F_2 weak (gametic and zygotic sterility) (7) F_1 completely sterile, F_2 none (gametic sterility)	vigorous	weak or none	genetic blocking in F_1 or F_2	
PARENTAL GENOMES BARELY ABLE TO COMBINE: (8) F_1 weak or none	weak or none	none		internal
PARENTAL GENOMES CANNOT COMBINE: (9) Hybrid zygote and endosperm do not fit together (10) Hybrid zygote and maternal cytoplasm do not fit together (11) Pollen tube too short or too wide (12) Pollen tube grows too slowly in foreign style (13) Pollen does not germinate on foreign stigma	none	none	genetic blocking before F_1 (if blocking overcome, may produce fertile F_2)	

Fig. 75. Kinds of isolating mechanisms that separate natural entities of various ranks.

sides of the Atlantic, Shull (1929) described several entities he regarded as species, including *occidentalis,* which according to the data from crossings is an early-blooming Mediterranean ecological race that is morphologically distinct from the later-blooming forms of typical *bursa-pastoris* from central and northern Europe. In a later paper Shull (1937) summarized the results of a study of more than 1600 strains of these entities collected on both sides of the Atlantic but grown at Princeton University. All strains from Oregon and Washington as well as from the midwestern and eastern United States were of the late-blooming *bursa-pastoris* type, similar to those from central and northern Europe on the opposite side of the Atlantic. On the other hand, the strains from central and southern California and Arizona were all of the early-blooming *occidentalis* type, like those from the Mediterranean countries in the Eastern Hemisphere. From the routes of communication between the two continents it is evident that *bursa-pastoris* and *occidentalis* were equally introduced to all of the states in western North America, but only the Mediterranean form became established in California, and only the central and northern European one in Oregon and Washington. Each fits its own specific environment, and neither has changed since its migration. On the one hand, we have the isolation by distance alone between the central European and northern United States *bursa-pastoris,* and likewise between Mediterranean and Californian *occidentalis.* On the other hand, both in Europe and in western North America there is the parallel distinction between the northern and southern ecological races. This latter difference falls in category 3 of the table shown in figure 75. Shull (1937) reports only one instance of a transition form, namely, one from Humboldt County in northern California, which in morphological characters was listed as *occidentalis* but developed slowly like *bursa-pastoris.* It is possible that this one may have resulted either from hybridization or from mutation.

Selection by different environments is added to spatial isolation in categories 2 to 4. The entities in these categories respond to environmental selection by genetic changes that fit the environment, and their external spatial isolation is therefore reinforced by genetic and physiologic fitness to certain environments and unfitness to others. Environmental selection is quite strong in the categories of selective pollination by different pollinating agents, in climatic and edaphic separation, and in seasonal races.

Categories 5 to 8 of figure 75 are those of increasing genetic blocking in F_2 and F_1, until the parental genomes are barely able to combine and the hybrid is barely able to survive. A great variety of patterns are included in these four categories, but in each case the nature of the isolating barrier is the genetic one of weak or inviable hybrid offspring. In each of these cases, the entity brings its barrier along wherever it moves. This barrier is therefore internal, and it may or may not be reinforced by a selective environmental barrier.

In categories 9 to 13 the parental genomes do not even combine, because there is genetic blocking even before the F_1 is produced. In category 9 the hybrid embryo and the endosperm do not fit together. In cases, however, where the hybrid embryo is excised and removed from the endosperm in an early stage, a fully vigorous and fully fertile F_1 and a normal F_2 can often be grown. This situation is exemplified by hybrids between species of *Linum* (Laibach, 1925, 1931) and of *Datura* (Blakeslee and Satina, 1944). Species thus separated never had an opportunity to develop genetic barriers in the F_1 or F_2, and when the blocking to crossing is overcome, their chromosomes are completely homologous and the F_1's and F_2's are fully fertile and vigorous.

Another variation in the pattern of separation through blocking of hybridization is found in category 10. The situation in certain *Epilobium* hybrids, in which the hybrid nucleus and the maternal cytoplasm do not fit together, suggested this category; if the unfitness had been a little greater we might never have seen the hybrid. Of a similar kind are chlorophyll disturbances in certain interspecific hybrids of *Geranium* (Dahlgren, 1923) and *Hypericum* (Noack, 1931), which affect only one of the reciprocals. Category 11, in which the pollen tube is too short, is structural and is exemplified by *Polemonium* (Ostenfeld, 1929) and *Zea-Tripsacum* crossings (Mangelsdorf and Reeves, 1939). Under experimental conditions this blocking can often be overcome either by removing a length of the long style or by making the crossing in the reciprocal direction. In the wild, this mechanism of separation is very effective.

Category 12, in which the pollen tube develops too slowly in the foreign style, represents a physiological and not a mechanical blocking, and it may indicate that the entities tested are evolutionarily very distinct. Gershoy (1932, 1934) described this pattern in the genus *Viola,* and he usually found it operative between entities that belong to distinct sections of the genus. Finally, category 13, in which the pollen tube does not even germinate on the foreign stigma, is characteristic of a great many phylogenetically very remote species that cannot be crossed at all.

There are a great many variants of isolating mechanisms, and the ones here classified are only examples. The general conclusion that can be drawn from such variety in modes of separation is that life has innumerable ways of accomplishing things, and it is difficult for us to encompass all the patterns by which species and other evolutionary entities have become isolated.

We find, accordingly, that in the evolution of plant species there is a long series of stages of increasing evolutionary distinctness, starting with the local populations, continuing through ecological races, ecospecies, and groups of species of higher and higher order within one comparium. It is only within these limits that we are able to analyze the nature and the organization of the evolutionary units by cytogenetic means. Many and varied are the evolutionary processes which are at work within such a comparium, but the evolutionary lines within it are those of a network; within the limits of the comparium evolution is still very active.

It seems probable that ecological races were the forerunners of species, and species the forerunners of species complexes or even genera. Many are the pulsating influences in time which tend to separate the entities through selection and to recombine them again through crossing until one comparium splits off from the others through major branching. From that time on, each comparium must depend upon its own resources for further evolution. We now know that the branches of the evolutionary tree should be represented as being hollow and containing the great, pulsating network of huge comparia with their species groups, species, ecological races or subspecies, and local populations, all with their great individual and potential variability. The future of an evolutionary branch depends upon the reservoir of variability which is stored within its natural entities. When a comparium or any other natural entity becomes depauperated through too much selection and too little variability, then it is on its way out, as has happened to so many groups of plants and animals in the past. When we consider the many intricate safeguards in the biological entities for preservation of variability, we conclude that the all-important law in biology is one of dissimilarity and variability, rather than of uniformity. In a biological sense uniformity is extremely dangerous.

The organization of living things in space and time— The question has often been asked whether living organisms are organized in a continuum or whether they are discontinuous. The answer is "both — and." The web of life projected through time appears to be a three-dimensional network and is a continuum, but at any one time level the species and genera are arranged in discontinuous groups.

Figure 76 is an attempt at a pictorial representation of the evolutionary relationships of two of the present-day genera of the *Madiinae, Layia* and *Madia.* The species of today are represented as cut, irregular cables composed of many intertwined strands, spatially arranged more or less according to their relationships and content of races. Below the present-day level the relationship is, of course, entirely hypothetical. Some new strands arise through convergence and intertwining of old strands, and others through the splitting of strands. Loose ends are being left off here and there where an evolutionary line has ended. The figure depicts the situation at a point where two genera have relatively recently branched off from each other but where it still is possible to connect one or two of the most vigorous species in the two genera by an occasional strand, as it actually is possible to do between *Layia* and *Madia.* The figure makes no attempt to present an over-all picture of the 85 species of the *Madiinae,* and leaves the other 30,000 species of the *Compositae* and the rest of the plant kingdom to the reader's imagination. Also, the depth in time is very slight, probably no more than 50,000 to 100,000 years.

In certain areas of the evolutionary network the cords come very close together; in other areas they are few and far between. Our "natural groups" represent our best estimate of the degree of discontinuity based upon morphology, ecology, distribution, chromosome number, and cytogenetics, but we do not require accurate knowledge of the projection of the strands into the past in order to recognize these relative discontinuities of present-day species.

If we follow the strands of such a network from an earlier period upward in time we will find a continuum, for the strands will run hither and yon, will aggregate here and there to huge, closely knit

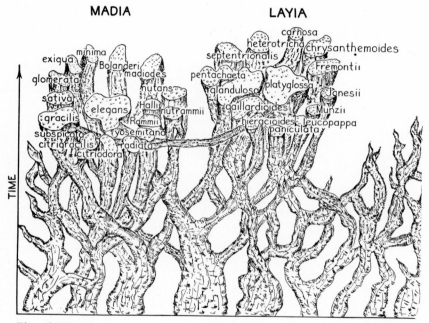

Fig. 76. Hypothetical reticulate evolutionary relationships between the species of the genera *Madia* and *Layia* in their present status and projected back in time. See text.

complexes which will be separated again as we follow them to another time level where other strands may aggregate to form a dense plexus. Through parallel variation two evolutionary strands that today are completely separated but which a hundred thousand years ago were together may still carry the evidence of interchange of genes that may have taken place a million years ago. Certain *Madia* species have no pappus, but they carry modifier genes that will modify the pappus of those species that have pappus. Such evidence suggests continuity between now completely distinct genera through their extinct ancestral lines.

Even though we may think we dimly see some of the organization in the intricate network that connects the life of today with that of the past, we still do not know what enables living things to develop as they do, or how they first came into being. The research of the present century has merely opened our eyes to see a remarkable and still quite incomprehensible organization of living things. Faced with such a situation, the scientist becomes humble, for at this point he meets the Great Unknown.

The Messenger Lectures

IN its original form this book consisted of lectures delivered at Cornell University in the fall of 1950, namely, the Messenger Lectures on the Evolution of Civilization. That series was founded and its title prescribed by Hiram J. Messenger, B.Litt., Ph.D., of Hartford, Connecticut, who directed in his will that a portion of his estate be given to Cornell University and used to provide annually a "course or courses of lectures on the evolution of civilization, for the special purpose of raising the moral standard of our political, business, and social life." The lectureship was established in 1923.

Bibliography

Babcock, E. B. 1947. The genus *Crepis*. Part I. The taxonomy, phylogeny, distribution, and evolution of Crepis. Berkeley and Los Angeles, University of California Press. x + 197 pp.

Babcock, E. B., and H. M. Hall. 1924. *Hemizonia congesta,* a genetic, ecologic, and taxonomic study of the hayfield tarweeds. Univ. Calif. Pub., Bot. 13:15–88.

Baker, M. S. 1935. Studies in western violets. I. Sections *Chamaemelanium* and *Nomimium*. Madroño 3:51–57.

———. 1948. A new western violet. Leafl. West. Bot. 5:101–102.

———. 1949. Studies in western violets. IV. Leafl. West. Bot. 5:141–147.

Baur, Erwin. 1924. Untersuchungen über das Wesen, die Entstehung, und die Vererbung von Rassenunterschieden bei *Antirrhinum majus*. Bibliotheca Genetica, Vol. 4. Leipzig, Gebr. Bornträger. 170 pp.

Blakeslee, A. F., and S. Satina. 1944. New hybrids from incompatible crosses in *Datura* through culture of excised embryos on malt media. Science 99:331–334.

Bonnier, Gaston. 1895. Recherches experimentales sur l'adaptation des plantes au climat alpin. Ann. des sci. nat. Botanique, 7th ser., 20:217–358.

Brainerd, Ezra. 1904. Hybridism in the genus *Viola*. Rhodora 6:213–223.

———. 1906a. Hybridism in the genus *Viola*. II. Rhodora 8:6–10.

———. 1906b. Hybridism in the genus *Viola*. III. Rhodora 8:49–61.

———. 1913. Four hybrids of *Viola pedatifida*. Bull. Torr. Bot. Club 40:249–260.

———. 1924. Some natural violet hybrids of North America. Vermont Agri. Exp. Sta. Bull. 239:1–205.

Cannon, W. A. 1902. A cytological basis for the Mendelian laws. Bull. Torr. Bot. Club 29:657–661.

Clausen, Jens. 1921. Studies on the collective species *Viola tricolor* L. Bot. Tidsskr. 37:206–221.

———. 1922. Studies on the collective species *Viola tricolor* L. II. Bot. Tidsskr. 37:363–416.

———. 1926. Genetical and cytological investigations on *Viola tricolor* L. and *V. arvensis* Murr. Hereditas 8:1–156. Also: Dissertation, University of Copenhagen, 1926.

———. 1927. Chromosome number and the relationship of species in the genus *Viola*. Ann. Bot. 41:677–714.

———. 1929. Chromosome number and relationship of some North American species of *Viola*. Ann. Bot. 43:741–764.

———. 1930. Inheritance of variegation and of black flower color in *Viola tricolor* L. Hereditas 13:342–356.

———. 1931a. Genetic studies in *Polemonium*. III. Preliminary account on the cytology of species and species hybrids. Hereditas 15:62–66.

———. 1931b. Cyto-genetic and taxonomic investigations on *Melanium* violets. Hereditas 15:219–308.

———. 1949. Genetics of climatic races of *Potentilla glandulosa*. Proc. Eighth Int. Congr. Genetics, Hereditas, Suppl. Vol., pp. 162–172.

Clausen, Jens., D. D. Keck, and W. M. Hiesey. 1939. The concept of species based on experiment. Am. Jour. Bot. 26:103–106.

———, D. D. Keck, and W. M. Hiesey. 1940. Experimental studies on the nature of species. I. Effect of varied environments on western North American plants. Carnegie Inst. Washington Pub. 520. vi + 452 pp. Second printing, 1950.

———, D. D. Keck, and W. M. Hiesey. 1941. Experimental taxonomy. Carnegie Inst. Washington Year Book no. 40:160–170.

———, D. D. Keck, and W. M. Hiesey. 1945. Experimental studies on the nature of species. II. Plant evolution through amphiploidy and autoploidy, with examples from the *Madiinae*. Carnegie Inst. Washington Pub. 564. vi + 174 pp. Second printing, 1950.

———, D. D. Keck, and W. M. Hiesey. 1947. Heredity of geographically and ecologically isolated races. Am. Nat. 81:114–133.

———, D. D. Keck, and W. M. Hiesey. 1948. Experimental studies on the nature of species. III. Environmental responses of climatic races of *Achillea*. Carnegie Inst. Washington Pub. 581, iii + 129 pp.

Cleland, R. E. 1949. Phylogenetic relationships in *Oenothera*. Proc. Eighth Int. Congr. Genetics, Hereditas, Suppl. Vol., pp. 173–188.

Correns, Carl. 1900. G. Mendel's Regel über das Verhalten der Nachkommenschaft der Rassenbastarde. Ber. Deutsch. Bot. Ges. 18:158–168.

Dahlgren, K. V. O. 1923. *Geranium bohemicum L. × G. bohemicum deprehensum* Erik Almq., ein grünweisses-marmorierter Bastard. Hereditas 4:239–250.

Darwin, Charles. 1859. On the origin of species by means of natural selection. London, John Murray.

Dobzhansky, Th. 1937, 1941. Genetics and the origin of species. New York, Columbia University Press. First ed., 364 pp. Rev. ed., 446 pp.

Gaertner, C. F. 1849. Versuche und Beobachtungen über die Bastarderzeugung im Pflanzenreich. Stuttgart. xvi + 790 pp.

Gershoy, Alexander. 1928. Studies in North American violets. I. General considerations. Vermont Agr. Exp. Sta., Bull. 279. 18 pp.

——. 1932. Descriptive notes for *Viola* exhibit. The *Nomimium* and *Chamaemelanium* sections. Sixth Int. Congr. Genetics. 27 pp. (Privately published by Gershoy. Printed by Vermont Agr. Exp. Sta., Burlington, Vt.)

——. 1934. Studies in North American violets. III. Chromosome numbers and species characters. Vermont Agr. Exp. Sta., Bull. 367. 91 pp.

Grant, Verne. 1950. The protection of ovules in flowering plants. Evolution 4:179–201.

——. 1951. Isolation and hybridization between *Aquilegia formosa* and *A. pubescens*. El Aliso 2: (in press).

Guyer, M. F. 1902. Hybridism and the germ cell. Bull. Univ. Cincinnati no. 21.

Huxley, J. S. 1940. Toward the new systematics. In J. S. Huxley, ed., *The New Systematics,* Oxford, Clarendon Press. pp. 1–46.

Jepson, W. L. 1923–1925. A manual of the flowering plants of California. Berkeley, Associated Students. 1238 pp.

Johannsen, Wilhelm. 1903. Über Erblichkeit in Populationen und in reinen Linien. Jena, Gustav Fischer. 68 pp.

——. 1905. Arvelighedslaerens Elementer. Copenhagen. viii + 254 pp.

——. 1911. The genotype conception of heredity. Am. Nat. 45:129–159.

Johansen, D. A. 1933. Cytology of the tribe *Madiinae,* family *Compositae.* Bot. Gaz. 95:177–208.

Jordan, Alexis. 1846. Observations sur plusieurs plantes nouvelles, rares ou critiques de la France. II. Ann. Soc. Linnéenne de Lyon.

——. 1873. Remarques sur le fait de l'existence en société à l'état sauvage des espèces végétales affines . . . Bull. ass. franç. avanc. d. sciences. 2. Session, Lyon.

Keck, D. D. 1935. Studies on the taxonomy of the *Madiinae*. Madroño 3:4–18.

Koelreuter, J. G. 1761–1766. Vorläufige Nachricht von einigen das Geschlecht der Pflanzen betreffenden Versuchen und Beobachtungen. Leipzig, 50 pp.; Fortsetzung, 72 pp.; Zweite Fortsetzung, 128 pp.; Dritte Fortsetzung, 156 pp. Also: Ostwald's Klassiker der exakten Wissenschaften. Nr. 41, 1893. Leipzig. 266 pp.

Kruckeberg, Arthur R. 1951. Intraspecific variability in the response of certain native plant species to serpentine soil. Am. Jour. Bot. 38:408–419.

Laibach, F. 1925. Das Taubwerden von Bastardsamen und die künstliche Aufzucht früh absterbender Bastardembryonen. Zeitschr. f. Bot. 17:417–459.

——. 1931. Über Störungen in den physiologischen Beziehungen zwischen Mutter und Embryo bei Bastardierung. Zeitschr. ind. Abst. u. Vererbungslehre 59:102–125.

Lawrence, W. E. 1947. Chromosome numbers in *Achillea* in relation to geographic distribution. Am. Jour. Bot. 34:538–545.

Linnaeus, Carolus. 1738. Classes Plantarum. Leyden.

——. 1774. Systema Vegetabilium. Thirteenth edition. Göttingen, J. C. Dietrich. iv + 844 pp.

——. 1790. Disquisitio de Sexu Plantarum. Amoenitates Academicae 10: 100–131. (Crossing experiments, submitted in 1760.) Partially translated in Conway Zirkle. The beginnings of plant hybridization. Philadelphia, University of Pennsylvania Press, 1935. p. 196.

Mangelsdorf, P. C., and R. G. Reeves. 1939. The origin of Indian corn and its relatives. Texas Agr. Exp. Sta. Bull. 574. 315 pp.

Manton, Irene. 1950. Problems of cytology and evolution in the *Pteridophyta*. Cambridge, Cambridge University Press. xi + 316 pp.

Mendel, G. 1865. Versuche über Pflanzenhybriden. Verhandl. naturf. Vereines, Brünn 4:3–47. Reprinted in Ostwald's Klassiker der exacten Wissenschaften. Nr. 121, 1901. Leipzig. 62 pp.

Miyaji, Yachigi. 1913. Untersuchungen über die Chromosomenzahlen bei einigen *Viola*-Arten. Bot. Mag., Tokyo 27:443–460. (Japanese.) Abstracted in German, 1927, in Bot. Mag. Tokyo 41:262–268.

——. 1929. Studien über die Zahlenverhältnisse der Chromosomen bei der Gattung *Viola*. Cytologia 1:28–58.

——. 1930. Betrachtungen über die Chromosomenzahlen von *Viola*, Violaceen und verwandten Familien. Planta 11:631–649.

Morgan, T. H. 1911. An attempt to analyze the constitution of the chromosomes, etc. Jour. Exp. Zool. 11:365–411.

——. 1915. Localization of the hereditary material in the germ cells. Proc. Natl. Acad. Sci. 1:420–429.

Muller, H. J. 1927. Artificial transmutation of the gene. Science 66:84–87.

——. 1928. The measurement of gene mutation rate in *Drosophila*, its high variability, and its dependence upon temperature. Genetics 13:279–357.

Noack, K. L. 1931. Über *Hypericum*-Kreuzungen. I. Die Panaschüre der Bastarde zwischen *Hypericum acutum* Moench und *Hypericum montanum* L. Zeitschr. ind. Abst. Vererbungslehre 59:77–101.

Ostenfeld, C. H. 1929. Genetic studies in *Polemonium*. II. Experiments with crosses of *P. mexicanum* Cerv. and *P. pauciflorum* Wats. Hereditas 12:33–40.

Rosenberg, Otto. 1903. Das Verhalten der Chromosomen in einer hybriden Pflanze. Ber. Deutsch. Bot. Ges. 21:110–119.

——. 1904. Über die Tetradenteilung eines *Drosera*-Bastardes. Ber. Deutsch. Bot. Ges. 22:47–53.

——. 1909. Cytologische und morphologische Studien an *Drosera longifolia* × *rotundifolia*. K. Svensk. Vetenskapsakad. Handl. 43, no. 11. 64 pp.

Shull, G. H. 1929. Species hybridizations among old and new species of shepherd's purse. Proc. Int. Congress, Plant Sci. 1:837–888.

——. 1937. The geographical distribution of the diploid and double-diploid species of shepherd's purse. Nelson Fithian Davis Birthday Volume. (Published privately in Boston, under chairmanship of Heber K. Youngken.) Pp. 1–8.

Sinskaya, E. N., and A. A. Beztuzheva. 1930–1931. The forms of *Camelina sativa* in connection with climate, flax and man. Bull. Appl. Genet. and Plant Breed. 25:98–200.

Stebbins, G. L., Jr. 1950. Variation and evolution in plants. New York, Columbia University Press. xix + 643 pp.

Sutton, W. S. 1902. On the morphology of the chromosome group in *Brachystola magna*. Biol. Bull. 4:24–39.

Sutton, W. S. 1903. The chromosomes in heredity. Biol. Bull. 4:231–251.

Tammes, Tine. 1925. Mutation und Evolution. Zeitschr. ind. Abst. u. Vererbungslehre 36:417–426.

Tedin, Olof. 1925. Vererbung, Variation und Systematik in der Gattung *Camelina*. Hereditas 6:275–386.

Tschermak, Erich. 1900. Über künstliche Kreuzung bei *Pisum sativum*. Ber. Deutsch. Bot. Ges. 18:232–239.

Turesson, Göte. 1922. The genotypic response of the plant species to the habitat. Hereditas 3:211–350.

——. 1925. The plant species in relation to habitat and climate. Hereditas 9:81–101.

——. 1931. The selective effect of climate upon plant species. Hereditas 15:99–152.

Vries, Hugo de. 1900. Sur la loi de disjonction des hybrides. Compt. Rend. Acad. Sci., Paris, 130:845–847.

——. 1901–1903. Die Mutationstheorie. Leipzig. I: v + 648 pp.; II: vi + 752 pp.

Winge, Öjvind. 1917. The chromosomes. Their number and general importance. Comp. rend. trav. Lab. Carlsberg 13:131–275.

——. 1925. Contributions to the knowledge of chromosome numbers in plants. La Cellule 35:303–324.

Wright, Sewall. 1932. The roles of mutation, inbreeding, crossbreeding and selection in evolution. Proc. Sixth Int. Congr. Genetics 1:356–366. Brooklyn, Brooklyn Botanic Garden.

——. 1940. Breeding structure of populations in relation to speciation. Am. Naturalist 74:232–248.

Index

Achillea, 30-45, 90, 161-164
    borealis, 32, 161-163
        distribution of, 43-44
        interracial hybrid of, 161
        range of tolerance of, related to
            variability, 22
        variation in, 21-22
    borealis × millefolium, 162-164
    chromosome numbers of, 32
    climatic races of, 30-43
    gigantea (= California Valley race of
        borealis), 32, 161-164
    interspecific hybrid of, 164
    lanulosa, 32
        distribution of, 43-44
        ssp. alpicola, 34
    millefolium, 162-164
    millefolium complex, 30
    number of ecologically distinct races,
        161
    parallel ecotypes, 43, fig. 16, p. 45
    variation across a transect, fig. 9, 33
amphiploid species, 117, 172
    characteristics of, 119, 172
    origin of, 117-120, fig. 51
amphiploidy, 131, 171, 172
    by addition of different genomes,
        166
    definition of, 8
    in Madia citrigracilis, 134
    in Madia nutrammii, 134
    in Viola praemorsa linguaefolia, 154
    in Viola utahensis, 155

partial, in Viola tricolor × arvensis,
    169
perpetuating the F_1 type, 172
Antirrhinum (snapdragon), spontaneous
    mutation in, 9
apomictic species, variation in, 12, 28
Aquilegia (columbine), 92-93
    caerulea, 93
    canadensis, 92
    formosa, 93
    formosa × pubescens, natural hybrid
        of, 93
    pubescens, 93
autoploidy, 159, 167

Babcock, E. B., 107, 112, 183
Baker, M. S., 61, 153, 183
balance, functional (see also equilib-
    rium)
    external, with environment, 170
    internal, 170
        characteristics of species, 165
        development of through selection,
            170
        developmental, 164
        genetic, 164
        metabolic, 164
        through physiological synchroniza-
            tion, 164
barriers (see also isolation)
    external, 174
    genetic

189